VINTAGE WOODWORKING MACHINERY

An Illustrated Guide to Four Manufacturers

VINTAGE WOODWORKING MACHINERY

An Illustrated Guide to Four Manufacturers

Dana M. Batory

With guides to buying and restoring by the author and David E. Pollak

ASTRAGAL PRESS
Mendham, New Jersey

Library of Congress Catalog Card Number: 97-70454
International Standard Book Number: 1-879335-75-1

Published by
THE ASTRAGAL PRESS
Mendham, New Jersey 07945

Manufactured in the United States of America

DEDICATION

To my brothers Bruce and Todd, two fine craftsmen.

TABLE OF CONTENTS

The Oliver Machinery Company

Buying Vintage Woodworking Machinery

Restoring Woodworking Machinery

A Note to the Reader

Bibliography

Introduction

The working of wood fundamentally impacts the character and quality of man's life as do few other of his endeavors. Developments in methods for working wood, therefore, have usually created large ripple effects upon the course of history throughout the ages. From the first use of the most primitive tool for shaping wood thousands of years ago, to the invention of sophisticated and multi-various woodworking machinery in the late nineteenth and early to mid twentieth century, major advances in working wood have usually triggered concurrent major developments in processes central to life, including shelter, transportation and industrial production.

This book focuses on four major American woodworking machine manufacturers: Fay & Egan, Yates-American, Defiance, and Oliver. It provides a brief history of each of these manufacturers, including a description of the evolution of its product lines over the years. In doing so, it chronicles the advancement of the industry from the treadle-powered machines of the 1850s to the intricate machinery of the 1920s and 30s, including boring, mortising and tenoning machines; lathes; molders and planers; band, rip, and scroll saws; cutoff table and trim saws; shapers, and trimmers.

Illustrations of, and specifications for, representative machines in various categories, taken from company catalogs of the period, are provided.

Finally, this book includes comprehensive chapters on buying and restoring vintage woodworking machinery for use today.

This book is intended as a guide for those interested in acquiring and using woodworking machinery, as well as for those simply interested in the technological developments realized by this critical American industry during its golden age.

ACKNOWLEDGEMENTS

A great many individuals and institutions assisted in my project and I would very much like to thank each of them.

I would particularly like to thank Cameron Brown of San Juan Bautista, California, and George M. Mustybrook of Rockford, Illinois, for taking an interest in my task and kindly supplying valuable research material and encouragement. I would also like to thank the staff of the Crestline (Ohio) Public Library for their heroic efforts in tracking down obscure books and periodicals and running off hundreds of copies.

A special thanks to the following:

For information on The J.A. Fay & Egan Co.:

Barbara E. Austen, Assistant Curator, New Hampshire Historical Society, Concord, New Hampshire

Jean Berg, Assistant Director, Keene (New Hampshire) Public Library

Cameron Brown, San Juan Bautista, California

Richard E. Cole, Hillsdale, Michigan

Barbara J. Dawson, Assistant Librarian, Cincinnati (Ohio) Historical Society

Judy Diers, Cincinnati, Ohio

Alfred Kleine-Kreutzmann, Curator of Rare Books & Special Collections, Public Library of Cincinnati and Hamilton County

Virginia H. Parr, Head, Reference/Bibliographic Services, Central Library, University of Cincinnati

David H. Shayt, Museum Specialist, Division of Mechanical & Civil Engineering, Smithsonian Institution

Conrad F. Weitzel, Reference Librarian, Archives-Library Division, Ohio Historical Society, Columbus, Ohio

Yeatman Anderson III, Curator of Rare Books & Special Collections, Public Library of Cincinnati, Ohio

Myers F. Yeomans, Cincinnati, Ohio

Ray Zwick, Librarian, *The Cincinnati Enquirer*

For information on the Yates-American Machine Co.:

  Linda Beyer, Information Librarian, Beloit (Wisconsin) Public Library

  Carol French, Director, Berlin (Wisconsin) Public Library

  William Kerfoot, Conowingo, Maryland

  Stuart Macuaig, Hamilton (Ontario) Public Library

  Joyce Stenler, Historian, Berlin, Wisconsin

For information on the Defiance Machine Works:

  Pat Little, Ohioana Room, Defiance (Ohio) Public Library

  Messerman Machine Co., Defiance, Ohio

  James Perry, Defiance, Ohio

  Louis Simonis, Defiance, Ohio

  Father John Stites, Walbridge, Ohio

  Richard Vaugh, Columbus, Ohio

  Wayne Yager, Churubusco, Indiana

For information on the Oliver Machinery Co.:

  Pamela Boynton, Michigan Room, Grand Rapids Public Library, Grand Rapids, Michigan

  Jay Dykstra, Product Sales Officer, Oliver Machinery Co., Grand Rapids, Michigan

  Michigan Department of Commerce, Corporation & Securities Bureau, Lansing, Michigan

  Oliver Machinery Co., Grand Rapids, Michigan

Chapter 1

THE J.A. FAY & EGAN COMPANY

"Best By Test"

"The J.A. Fay & Egan Company," wrote the editor of *Cincinnati – The Queen City* (1914), "leads the world in the manufacture of woodworking machinery. Its salesmen traverse the globe. . ."

The J.A. Fay & Egan Co. was once the largest, oldest, and most influential maker of woodworking machinery in the world. It supplied the growing needs of industry from Victorian times through the Roaring Twenties. Those were the days when plastics and cardboard boxes were a rarity, when everything was packaged and shipped in wooden boxes or barrels, vehicles (including automobiles) were made of wood, bridges and trestles were built of timber, and of course there were wooden furniture, houses, agricultural implements, machinery, etc.

Cincinnati, Ohio, located on the Ohio River, was chartered as a village in 1802 and incorporated as a city in 1819. Known as "The Queen City" and "The Gateway to the South," it has long been famous for building steamships, furniture, machine tools, and woodworking machinery.

The J.A. Fay & Egan Co. was nearly as old as the city. The company could truthfully boast that it was the world's oldest manufacturer of woodworking machines and one of the first choices of master cabinetmakers: "Best By Test" – as one of its early advertisements read.

Company roots actually reached back to 1830, when Jerub Amber ("Jemb") Fay (born 1808) began building tenoning machines for use in his cabinet shop and planing mill in Keene, New Hampshire. He soon recognized their potential market and began to produce them commercially.

During those first few years, Fay himself loaded his machines onto a wagon and made the rounds of the area's many woodworking shops selling them.

A short distance away, in South Keene, George Page was also busy. A prolific inventor, Page's fame comes from having invented the first foot powered mortising machine. Between 1830 and 1833, Page secured a patent and, with the financial backing of Thomas M. Edwards, made mortising machines under the name of T.M. Edwards & Company.

In 1834, local businessman Edward Joslin (or Josslyn) joined Page and Edwards. As the business grew it became necessary to enlarge its manufacturing facilities. In 1836, in order to obtain the benefit of water power, the group brought inventor and iron worker Aaron Davis into the partnership. They bought one half of Davis's business, turned his hoe factory in South Keene into a machine shop, and built a second story onto the plant.

That same year Fay acquired the interests of Davis, Page, and Edwards, and the firm became J.A. Fay & Company (sometimes also known as Joslin & Fay). Together Fay and Joslin not only improved the mortising machine but soon introduced the first powered mortising, tenoning, and molding machines ever made. The company made single end tenoners with cutterheads instead of saws as early as the 1840s. One such machine was shown by Fay & Co. at the Great Exhibition of 1851 in London.

In 1853, Fay & Co. purchased the Tainter & Childs shop at Worcester, Massachusetts, which was manufacturing the Daniels' wood planer. Much of Worcester's prominence as a manufacturing center was due to the unusual facilities it offered to enterprising mechanics just starting out in small-scale business. Almost every manufacturing concern in the city had begun in modest, rented quarters. Worcester had a number of large buildings that leased space with power to these small businesses. Famous early machine tool builders such as Coes, Flagg, Daniels, Wood, Light & Company, Coombs, Lathe & Morse, Whitcomb, Pond, and Fay, all started, or at some time operated, this way. Such New England shops were the 19th century equivalent of today's incubator factories.

In 1847, to meet the large demand for their machines, Fay and Joslin opened branch factories at Norwich, Connecticut, and Cincinnati, Ohio. The various branches soon became major factories in their own right – the one in Cincinnati being the largest.

At the 1851 World's Fair in London, the woodworking machinery exhibits consisted chiefly of Fay & Co., Furness of Liverpool (England), and one or two from the Continent. Fay & Co. took home a medal.

In 1852, the company built a new two-story brick mill (300 by 75 feet), with a large brick wing, at South Keene. A broadside from ca. 1853 lists its line of machinery: sash, molding and slat machines; tenoning machines; mortising and boring machines; power mortising machines; Daniels' Improved Planing Machine; Wells' Patent Saw Mill; and scroll saws. It also listed all the branch factories and their managers: Keene, New Hampshire, J.A. Fay and E. Joslin; Norwich, Connecticut, C.B. Rogers; Worcester, Massachusetts, E.C. Tainter; and Cincinnati, Ohio, John Cheney. All the branches' business affairs were conducted separately from the parent firm.

Fay died April 25, 1854, in Richmond, Virginia. His widow, however, continued on in the business with the other partners.

In 1856 C.B. Rogers wrote *The Mechanic's Companion and Builder's Guide; Or, Hand-Book of Wood Working Machinery,* which was published on behalf of the proprietor, J.A. Fay & Co. The volume contained a complete set of designs for moldings, architraves, bases, etc., and useful tables for mechanics. An 1856 catalog and price list included in the Guide listed Fay & Co.'s complete line of woodworking machinery, some 56 machines. The catalog also stated that each of the four plants made a different class of machinery.

By 1856 the company had been awarded nearly 50 medals, including awards at the 1851 World's Fair for the best woodworking machinery (for the sash and molding, foot mortising, and Daniels planing machines).

Like those of all early American manufacturers of woodworking machinery, almost all of Fay's machines had wooden frames. A typical example was the American Eagle Sash and Molding Machine. Available in two sizes, the machine was made for sticking (cutting to profile) all kinds of sash, both pine and hardwood; for moldings, from the smallest size up to four inches; for rabbeting; for planing blind-slats; and as a thickness planer. The frame was made of 5" x 5" well seasoned hard maple or birch timber. The cutterhead shafts were made of cast steel and ran in Babbitt's Improved Patent Boxes. The knives were made of the best double refined English cast steel, manufactured to order and imported by Fay & Co.

The basic large model American Eagle sold for $150. The foot mortising machine, which made the company's reputation and received the first premiums from the American Institute, several state fairs, and the prize medal in 1851, sold for $40. The company had the names of hundreds of carpenters, joiners, sash and blind makers, car builders, cabinetmakers, pianoforte manufacturers, etc., on file attesting to the mortiser's high merits. There were over 6000 in use throughout the world at the time.

The 1856 catalog also alerted its customers to some of the shady business practices of the day: "There is still another class of persons who have formerly acted as agents for us, and under that guise are now offering imitations of our machines, calling them the Fay & Co. Machines, and recommending them for use, simply because the manufacturers, in order to make sales of their imitations, are willing to pay such agents a larger commission on their articles."

An 1860 catalog issued by the company illustrated 73 woodworking machines, plus other products. Fifty of the woodworking machines used frames built of hardwood with metal brackets; the remainder were of cast iron.

In 1861, perhaps due to a decline in business caused by the outbreak of the Civil War, the partners decided to dissolve the firm. The western agents, headed by W.H. Doane, who had been with Fay & Co. since 1851, bought the name, the plants, and the product line and continued manufacturing in Cincinnati and Norwich.

Ads from 1866 reveal a portion of Fay & Co.'s machine line of that time: wheel, felloe, and spoke machinery; spoke lathes; hub mortising and boring machines; Woodworth Patent Planing and Matching Machines; siding and resawing machinery.

The company exhibited several machines at the 1878 International Exhibition in Paris: a combined hand feed planer (a jointer) and a power feed planer; a fret saw; a saw-setting machine; a dovetailing machine patented by Stengel; and the most complete band saw entered. The Improved Daniels' Planing Machine was still listed in the company catalog but was now available with iron or wood framing.

In 1880 the company introduced an improved Blanchard copying lathe, a machine for boring and mortising blind stiles in pairs, a self-feeding tenoning machine, and a self-feeding gang edger.

The *Carriage Monthly* and *The Hub*, trade journals devoted to the carriage industry, ran advertisements in 1888 for the Egan Co.'s woodworking machinery, shown on p.7.

Now is a good time to introduce Thomas P. Egan, founder of another great woodworking machinery company. Egan was born in Ireland on November 20, 1847. When he was still an infant,

his parents crossed the Atlantic and settled in Hamilton, Ontario, Canada. In 1863 Egan quit his job as a dry goods clerk and came to the United States, where he went to work operating a metalworking lathe for William Kirkup, a Cincinnati brass foundryman and manufacturer of brass goods.

After three months Egan left for Steptoe, McFarlan & Company, manufacturers of an extensive line of machine tools, mechanics' tools, and woodworking machinery. Two weeks later he lost his left arm in an accident. Instead of being dismissed (the usual practice), he was given a position in the office.

Egan worked continuously for several years, and in 1868 the company suggested he take a vacation. Instead, he asked to be sent out on the road as a company representative. Returning to Cincinnati after the first season, he was pleasantly surprised to discover that his sales surpassed those of the other agents. Egan continued as a salesman for seven more years, resigning in 1874 to start his own business.

Along with two partners, he rented space from his former employers and began manufacturing woodworking machinery. In 1874 almost every business in the United States suffered because of the Great Depression, but the Egan Company ended the year with a profit.

Each year saw an increase in sales. The company became an important name in the field of woodworking machinery. In 1881 the Egan Company was formally incorporated with a capital stock of $150,000. Egan was elected president and had near total control over its affairs. Soon sales were international in scope.

One machine made in the late 1880s was Egan Co.'s Improved 6 Inch Sticking Machine, also known as a one-sided horizontal molder. The machine had a one-piece cast iron frame, with the bed gibbed into the frame. The table could be lowered (dropped) 16" for working base boards or very wide lumber. The cast steel arbor ran in self-oiling boxes lined with genuine Babbitt metal, the steel head slotted on all four sides, and the stocker had a geared power feed.

Egan's increasing success made him a rival of his giant neighbor directly across the street. And in the grand tradition of American commerce, Fay & Co. apparently decided to drive Egan out of business by destroying his product line with a series of lawsuits claiming patent infringement.

The field was rich for litigation. The Egan Co. controlled some 175 patents and Fay & Co. about 200. Between them they accounted for practically every patent pertaining to woodworking machinery. Their suits and countersuits continued until 1893. The litigation cost both companies dearly. On one particular occasion, the Egan Co. carried its case up to the United States Supreme Court and won. Egan was too tough a nut for Fay to crack.

In February 1893 David Jones and H.B. Morehead obtained options for the controlling interest of both firms. Negotiations were begun that resulted in the merger of the two firms under the name The J.A. Fay & Egan Co., incorporated under the laws of West Virginia, March 1, 1893.

The new company was capitalized for $2,500,000; T.P. Egan was elected president and S.P. Egan, general superintendent. The two constituent companies operated independently, even though officered by the same men. At the 1893 World's Columbian Exposition in Chicago, each had separate exhibits and each received nine awards, with one special grant award, more than were received by any other company at the exhibition.

One of the J.A. Fay machines was a 26" x 5" double surface medium weight planer. The frame was of heavy cast iron plate sides and ends, with a wide and firm hollow core cast iron base. The two knife cutterheads were made of solid forged steel, with long journals 1¾" in diameter. The upper was supplied with a pulley at each end for using two belts to provide ample power. The four large feed rolls were connected by heavy gearing, producing a powerful and positive feed. The in-feed rolls were provided with adjustable weights for varying pressure, while the out-feed rolls had spring pressure.

They were enclosed to protect them from dust and shavings.

Two feed rates were provided, 21 and 36 feet per minute; the feed started and stopped by a lever and belt tightener acting on the slack side of the belt.

The pressure bars on each side of the upper cutterhead were self-acting. The one in front would rise and fall with the in-feed roller, always maintaining the same relative position, yet allowing it to yield to any inequalities in the lumber's surface. The bar controlling pressure after the cut was adjustable, allowing short pieces to be planed without clipping. The bar after the cut of the lower cutterhead was adjustable to meet the cut being made. The cast iron bed was gibbed to the frame, with provisions for taking up wear. It could be quickly raised or lowered to suit different lumber thicknesses.

Egan, the former $2 a week store clerk, now headed the largest company of its kind in the entire world. It employed 1000 hands and its plant was one of the largest and best equipped in America. Egan retired around 1912 and died in 1922 at the age of 74. His three sons and a brother continued in management roles at the company. The two houses continued to conduct their own businesses, both domestic and foreign, through their own representatives, for several years.

Fay & Egan had a hand in fathering much of Cincinnati's machine tool industry, launching on their careers many of the founders and early officers of the city's tool firms. (Henry Bickford, for example, an employee of J.A. Fay & Co., went on to form the Bickford Drill Co. in 1887.)

In 1895 the company was offering over 1000 different machines, including every size and type of woodworking machine, from the smallest scroll saws to the very largest dimension planers, car sill and timber dressing machines, and band saw mills; it could completely fit out any kind of woodworking factory on short notice.

The workforce of 1000 was constantly employed. Sales branches were operated in New York, New Orleans, Chicago, St. Louis, and San

Francisco; and in London, Amsterdam, Brussels, Copenhagen, Sydney, Melbourne, and Santiago. There were representatives in Berlin, Constantinople, and the principal cities of South America, Italy, Spain, and Mexico. The first combined catalog was issued circa 1900.

A quick look at Fay & Egan's 1902 catalog shows a wide range of machinery. The famous "Lightning Line" was yet to appear and machines were still being sold under the separate Fay Co. and Egan Co. nameplates.

A few years ago I was fortunate enough to purchase a Model 61 Lightning Line 16-inch jointer (circa 1912) made by Fay & Egan; I was thoroughly impressed with the quality of its engineering, craftsmanship, and the materials used.

The Model 61 is a typical "Lightning Line" machine. Patented March 29, 1911, the machine came in five sizes: 8, 12, 16, 20, and 24 inches. When equipped with the optional circular cutterhead, it was designated the Model 61-C.

Painted coal black, the fully adjustable, large infeed and outfeed tables are of heavily ribbed cast iron, the bed measuring a full 7 feet long. The rear table has a rabbeting ledge. The circular, two-knife cutterhead and shaft are turned from a solid steel forging, and rotate in babbitt bearings. The massive center-mounted cast iron fence permits jointing of extra long stock. It is fully adjustable across the width of the machine and can also be set at an angle for shear cutting. There are positive stops at 45o and 90o. The large, spring-loaded guard is one piece cast aluminum. The heavy iron base is cast in one piece with a broad floor support. A cast iron door opens into the hollow casting for a convenient tool cupboard. Big and rugged, weighing close to 1000 pounds, it was intended for years of accurate, heavy production work.

In 1920 the company introduced a double end automatic corner locking machine.

In 1923 Fay & Egan moved from the deteriorating West Front Street district to suburban Oakley, and into one of the city's largest plants, a one story, saw-tooth type building with 200,000 square feet of space occupying 15 acres of land. Nearly 500 workers were employed at the new factory. At this time the firm not only manufactured woodworking equipment but machine tools as well, and continued its practice of rebuilding and selling used equipment.

From a product line that had started with just four models, it now sold four hundred. Materials used in the machines had gone from wood, through iron, to steel. Babbitt bearing machines, with a maze of belts powered by a line shaft, had evolved into modern, ball-bearing motorized machines. Worldwide company agencies numbered ninety and the company's "Lightning Line" trademark had become known to craftsmen of almost every nation.

Fay & Egan briefly entered the aviation field in 1928, designing a profiler to cut propeller blades from wooden blanks. In 1930 a subsidiary, the Fay-Egan Manufacturing Company, was set up to produce aluminum propellers.

By 1928, Fay & Egan began losing money and continued to do so. Competition, coupled with the depression of 1929, struck it a blow from which it never quite recovered. Even so, it celebrated its 100th anniversary with proper ceremony in December 1929. By 1937, however, company losses were estimated at $500,000. Things looked grim.

On January 5, 1937, the company filed a petition in the United States District Court for reorganization under the National Bankruptcy Act. After weathering a petition from a bondholder calling for the complete dissolution of the firm, Fay & Egan filed new articles of incorporation in 1938, marking the mechanical phase of the company's reorganization. Later that year Cincinnati industrialist Walter E. Schott purchased the company from the Egan family and began stripping the company of various assets. He retained, however, the woodworking machinery operation; the company also still possessed a Used Machinery Division which would buy, sell, rebuild, and trade all makes and models of woodworking machinery.

By 1953 the company had moved into a small plant with 27,000 square feet of production and office space. Its Lightning Line still carried a variety of universal tilt arbor saws, single spindle shapers, high speed tenoners, heavy duty band saws, scroll saws, drop bed molders, single surface planers, and production band resaws. Fay & Egan continued to pride itself on being the leader in building the finest precision band saws and resaws. By 1956, however, the firm was making only twenty types of heavy industrial woodworking machinery.

The Company suffered a terrible blow in November 1957 when a two-alarm fire swept through and completely gutted its warehouse and valuable foundry patterns were lost.

In 1963 the company was purchased from the Schott family for over $1 million by a group of employees headed by general manager Gabriel. "There will be no interruption in our business," Gabriel boldly promised, "but a new and vigorous sales and promotional campaign will be initiated."

But it was not to be. In 1977, three years short of its 150th anniversary, Fay & Egan was turned over to Ohio Valley Machinery Inc., used machine-tool distributors, for liquidation. Ohio Valley not only offered the complete drawings, patterns, jigs, and other fixtures of a long list of Fay & Egan machinery, but also sold the large hoard of woodworking machinery acquired by the used machinery division.

Sadly, the J.A. Fay & Egan Co. ceased to exist that year, when it was purchased by James A. Wulfeck, a Cincinnati businessman who wished to assure that the thousands of old and discontinued woodworking machines could still be serviced.

Messrs. Fay and Egan's venerable company had lived a full, useful life; and Mr. Wulfeck's purchase and the creation of Dels Inds, based in Cincinnati, was intended to enable the old machines to carry out their duties faithfully, perhaps well into the next century. However, it is rumored that in 1985, for some inexplicable reason, most of Fay & Egan's records, blueprints, catalogs, etc., were cast into an incinerator.

Dels Inds itself is no longer listed in any directory. To the best of the author's knowledge, parts and service are no longer available commercially.

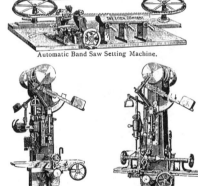

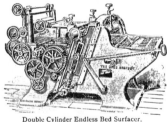

No. 2 Horizontal Boring Machine.

30-inch Double Drum Sander.

No. 2 Band Saw.

No. 3½ Double Spindle Shaper.

No. 1 Tenoning Machine.

Disk Sander, for Carriage Work, Bodies, &c.

Wheel Boxing Machine.

No. 4½ Band Scroll and Re-saw, Scrolling Adjustment.

No. 4½ Band Scroll and Re-saw, Re-sawing Adjustment.

THE EGAN COMPANY,
BUILDERS OF
WOOD-WORKING MACHINERY
For Carriage and Wagon Builders, Hub, Spoke
and Wheel Manufacturers,
196 to 216 W. FRONT STREET, CINCINNATI, OHIO, U.S.A.

The largest Carriage and Wagon Manufacturers in the world use our Tools almost Exclusively. Write for Catalogue and Prices.

Self-Feed Railway Cut-Off Saw.

Automatic Band Saw Setting Machine.

Double Cylinder Endless Bed Surfacer.

Variety Saw.

No. 4 Mortiser and Borer, Graduated Stroke.

Hub Mortiser and Borer, Graduated Stroke.

Automatic Spoke Lathe.

Universal Rip and Cross-Cut Saw.

Double Sanding Belt.

No. 1 Horizontal Borer.

7

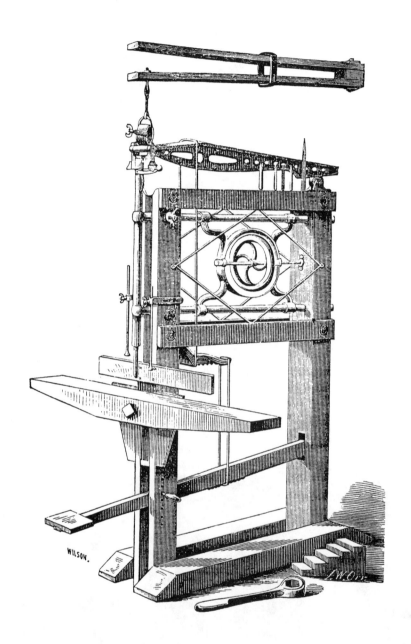

FOOT MORTISING MACHINE

The Mechanic's Companion and Builder's Guide-1856 —See next page

The following extras apply both to our large and small Foot Machines:

The Double Chisel for Sash Work.—It has two edges, with a V shape between. It is pressed into the sash-bar a little more than half-way through, when the bar is turned, and, by an impression on the opposite side, the mortise is made.

The Blind-slat Chisel is used for making the groove for the blind-slat in the stile, the length of which being less than the width of the stile, and corresponding with the width of the slat. The slat enters this groove, and is by it confined in its place without mouldings or brads. These chisels we make with one, two, or three pair of cutters, of such length and thickness as may be wanted.

The Pin-tool and Pointer makes both hard and soft wood pins for sash, blinds, doors, &c., varying in size from a quarter to three-eighths of an inch. Pine pins are pointed in the pointer by one blow from a hammer.

Standard Rolls, for door-stiles and larger work, are made ot play into a small iron frame, from which extends a bolt which is passed through a slot in an upright joist, about three and a half inches square, and by a thumb-nut on the end of the bolt the iron frame is confined to the upright, at an elevation corresponding with the level of the *rest* of the machine on which the piece to be mortised is placed, and by these rolls is easily moved as the chisel cuts away.

The Extra Rest, to mortise through from one side is confined to the *main rest* by a single bolt, and has a piece of very hard wood, standing endwise, which receives the edge of the chisel after it has passed through the blind-stile. This rest is made to move endwise on the main rest, so that when one place becomes worn by the long-continued action of the edge of the chisel, it is changed to the extent of the width of the endwise piece. The mortising of blind-stiles is the most suitable work to be done in this way.

Staple-punch for Blind-rods and Slats.—This tool is inserted in the machine in place of the chisel, and by the pressure of the foot two holes are made for the small staple.

CASH PRICES.

Large Foot Mortising Machine, with ¼, ⅜, 7/16, ½, ⅝ chisels		$40 00
Extra chisels, ⅛ to 1 inch	each	62½
" over 1 inch	"	1 00
Double sash-chisels	"	1 00
Pin-tools and pointers	"	1 00
Blind-slat chisels, single cutters	"	3 00
" " double cutters	"	3 75
" " treble cutters	"	4 50
Standard rolls	per pair	2 00
Extra rests to mortise through		2 00
Staple-punch, for slats	each	1 00
Hub apparatus		15 00

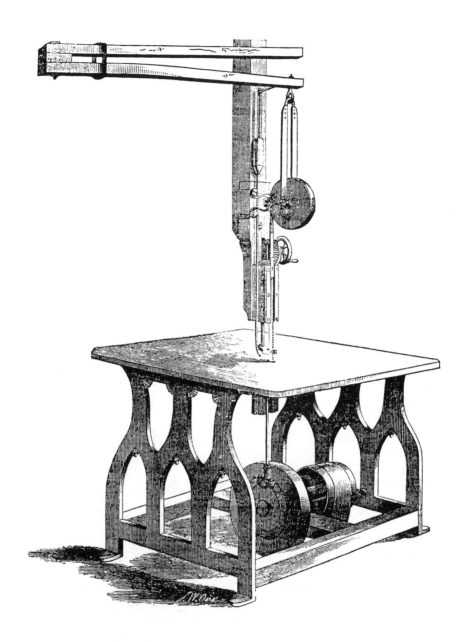

**IMPROVED SCROLL SAW
WITHOUT A GATE**

The Mechanic's Companion and Builder's Guide-1856—See next page

The ordinary kind of gate saws being so very inconvenient for most kinds of scroll sawing, has induced us to invent and perfect a scroll saw to work without any gate, by which a considerable saving is made in the amount of timer sawed—not requiring to be cut into short pieces before sawing. Another advantage over the gate saw is, that they may be run at a greater speed without trembling, as the upper and lower slides by which the saw is attached weighs only about one pound.

One important advantage of this over all other kinds of gate saws is, that no part of the frame is in the way of turning the stuff while sawing. Instead of overhanging the saw, ours are hung perpendicular, and the ways so arranged, that in the movement of the saw down, it moves forward three-sixteenths of an inch, by which the work is sawed square with the face, and requires much less labor in smoothing up for use.

We have also, by a very ingenious contrivance, succeeded in equalizing the strain or lateral tension of the saws when in use. This consists in the use of the spring, lever, pulley, and cam combined, by which the strain can be increased or diminished at pleasure, according to the kind of work, and size of the saw—the tension being at all times equal, whether passing down or up, when in use.

The tight and loose pulleys are 8½ inches diameter, 3½-inch face, and should make 350 revolutions per minute.

PRICE.

Scroll saw, complete, with twelve saws, assorted $75 00

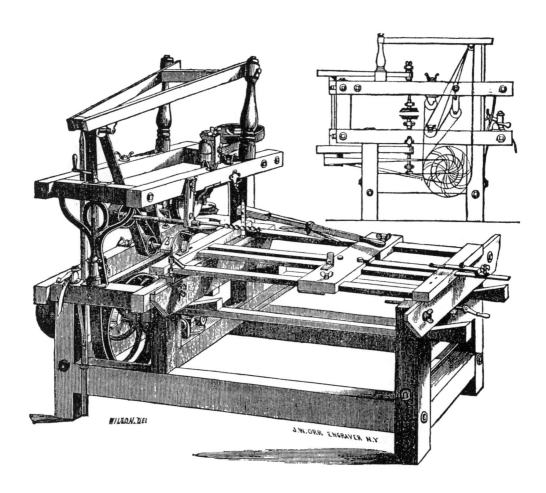

WILSON. DEL

J.W.ORR ENGRAVER N.Y.

MEDIUM SIZE TENONING MACHINE

THIS machine is provided with double cutters, and is particularly adapted to the manufacture of doors and long tenons. Each head is supplied with two sets of cutters, so adjusted as to cut a tenon six inches long at one operation. It is three inches longer than the common size, has all the late improvements, and is the most suitable machine to receive the double copes. In cutting door tenons, it will do the work of fifteen men.

The tight and loose pulleys are 12 inches in diameter, and 3¼-inch face, and require to make 525 revolutions per minute, giving the cutter-heads 2,360.

PRICE.

Medium size Tenoning Machine	$112 00
Upper and lower copes, if wanted	20 00
Boring apparatus and bits	13 50
Extension-rod	2 00
Pannel gauge	2 00
Boxing, when necessary	5 00
Total	$154 50

The Mechanic's Companion and Builder's Guide-1856

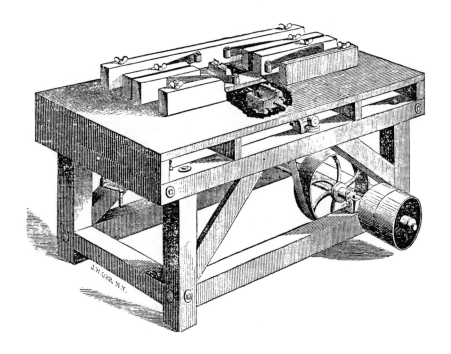

SMALL MATCHING MACHINE

This is a very simple machine, and well adapted to tongueing and grooving short stuff for boxes, sheathing, and other light work. It has a strong and neatly-made wood frame, four and a half feet long, two feet wide, and of convenient height. It is provided with two heads, one for tongueing and the other for grooving, which run upon the same arbor, under the table, which may to raised or lowered according to the depth of the work required, and a counter-shaft for getting up speed. The heads will receive cutters for working any thickness of stuff up to 2¼ inches.

The stuff which is passed over the heads by hand is gauged by adjustable guides being held against them by springs having friction-rolls attached. Both edges of the stuff is worked without any change in the position of the operator.

This machine requires a motion of about 3,500, and the belt-pulley on the counter-shaft is 9½ inches in diameter, and should make 900 revolutions.

Price of Machine . . $58 00   Boxed . . . $60 00

The Mechanic's Companion and Builder's Guide-1856

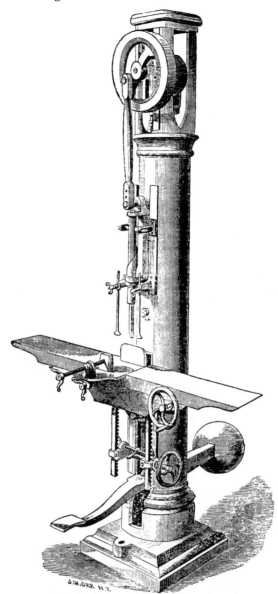

POWER MORTISING MACHINE

THIS machine may be driven by steam, water, or horse power. When put in operation, the chisel receives a rapid perpendicular motion, and on being brought down to the work by the foot, makes one end of the mortise, when the foot is removed, and the chisel carried up by a balance-weight on the opposite end of the treadle, and reversed by a cam on the slide. It is then brought down again, and the mortise is completed.

The machine may be kept in continued motion while doing any amount of work, as it does not require to be stopped in changing the stuff.

For mortising doors, and all kinds of work in soft wood, no boring is required for the mortise.

This machine is used to great advantage by door, sash, and blind makers, coach and car builders, manufacturers of agricultural implements, &c.

The driving-pulley is 10 inches in diameter, and 3¼-inch face, and should make 300 revolutions per minute. See next page. Price complete, with ¼, ⅜, ⁷⁄₁₆, ½, ⅝ in. chisels. $118.00.

The Mechanic's Companion and Builder's Guide-1856

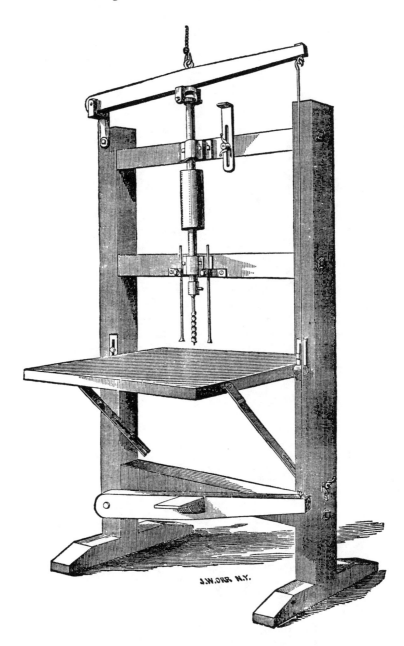

CHAIR BORING MACHINE

This machine has a frame consisting of two upright posts, three feet apart, between which the bed or table is hung on pivots or journals in boxes, and can be elevated at any angle desired, and held by thumbscrews.

The bit-shaft is upright, and the movement is made by the foot upon a treadle.

It is very convenient for any kind of boring, but more especially for chair or agricultural work requiring the holes to be made on an angle or obliquely from the working face.

PRICE.

Upright Chair Boring Machine $35 00
Bits fitted, per quarter 15

The Mechanic's Companion and Builder's Guide-1856

THE J.A. FAY & EGAN COMPANY

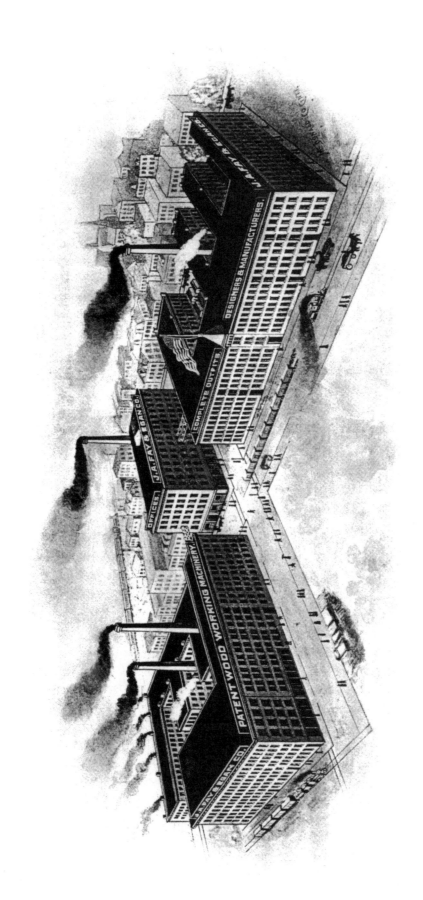

Office and Works of the J. A. Fay & Egan Co.

Occupying Three Entire Blocks at Front and John Streets, Cincinnati, Ohio, U. S. A.

J.A. Fay & Egan Co. Catalog Series L ca.1900

16

Safety Sealed
No. 560—All Electric—Ball Bearing—Two Speed
Single Cylinder Surfacer

A general utility surfacer of unique design to produce a high grade finish on either hard or soft wood and is adapted to a wide range of work in factories of all kinds. The new type construction all revolving parts enclosed in the "Safety Sealed" Cabinet Column makes it an ideal machine for the modern millroom.

CAPACITY: Will work up to 24" wide and 8" thick.

CYLINDER: Three-knife, full round and runs in Precision "Closely Fitted" Ball Bearings. Micrometer adjusting screws in the head control the accurate setting of the knives.

TABLE: Raises and lowers on large screws mounted on Ball Thrust Bearings by means of hand wheel convenient to operator.

FEED: Consists of four rolls, all driven. The upper Feed-in Roll fluted. Two speeds of feed, 18 and 30 feet a minute are obtained by means of Hardened Steel Sliding Clutch Gears operated by lever at front of column.

JOINTING AND SETTING DEVICES: Are regularly furnished. A Setting Pin is provided to hold cylinder in position for setting and grinding the knives in the head.

ELECTRIC DRIVE: Regularly furnished as full electric type having 5 h. p., 3600 r. p. m. motor mounted direct on cylinder, Push Button "Start and Stop" built in frame at operator's convenience.

BELT DRIVE: Machine may also be arranged for Belt Drive with taper fitted pneumatic cylinder pulley and with countershaft having tight and loose pulleys 10" diameter, 5½" face and should make 1200 r. p. m.

EQUIPMENT: Regular Motor Driven Machine is furnished complete ready to run with set of knives, jointing and setting devices and necessary wrenches, merely requiring connection to power lines.

No.	Size	Floor Space	H.P.	C.M.
560	24"	44" x 65"	5	90

Sectional Roll and Chipbreaker in 2" sections (extra).

No. 490—Ball Bearing—Electric
Single Cylinder Surfacer

DESIGNED for general light work in jobbing shops, furniture, sash and door, and box-making establishments, and makes an ideal machine for the manual training schools. This model supersedes the popular No. 2 Centennial Surfacer in lines only, a machine which has so wonderfully held the confidence of its operators only, a machine which has so meritorious performance. Made in two sizes, 16" and 24" wide, and 6" thick.

FRAME cast in one piece. Bed adjustable in gibbed ways by crank. Cylinder is of the three knife full-round type with thin air-hardened "Tungsten" steel knives, including jointing and setting device. Upper feed rolls driven, gears cut from the solid and enclosed. Feed 15' and 25' per minute. Center to center of feed rolls 9". Tight and loose pulleys on countershaft 10" x 4½" on the 16", and 10" x 5½" on the 24" to make 900 r. p. m.

DRIVE: For alternating current 2 or 3 phase, 60 cycle, 110, 220 or 440 volts motor is mounted direct on cylinder as above illustrated. Where A. C. is not available motor is coupled direct to cylinder or belted to cylinder as preferred.

COUNTERSHAFT: When furnished with countershaft tight and loose pulleys are 10" x 4½" on the 16" and 10" x 5½" on the 24" machine and make 900 r. p. m.

EQUIPMENT: Regularly furnished with one set of three knives and necessary wrenches: Countershaft included on Belt Drive.

No.	Size	Floor Space without C.S.	H.P.	C.M.
490	16"	3' 5" x 3' 6"	5	60
490	24"	4' 1" x 3' 6"	5	68

Sectional Roll and Chip Breaker in 2" sections (extra)............
Push Button Control (extra).

These details are constantly subject to change as improvement directs

No. 147—Double Cylinder Surfacer

DESIGNED for general surfacing in planing mills, carriage, wagon, furniture, cabinet, chair and box factories. Surfaces 24″, 30″ wide and 6″ thick.

FRAME is a heavy cast iron structure, open style.

BED raises and lowers in wide ways by powerful screws on ball bearings.

CYLINDERS are solid steel forgings, two-sided, and tapped, our new semi-round type, and are set very close together to insure accurate parallel work. Lower cylinder draws out at side of machine for setting and sharpening knives, and has independent vertical adjustment of entire housing with receiving and delivery bars adjustable by hand wheel directly under bed at feed-in end. Our Patented Circular Cylinders with self-hardening steel knives optional, including Setting and Jointing attachment which secures the highest efficiency from these thin steel knives.

PRESSURE BARS are adjustable vertically. One before the cut is made in four sections, permitting the operator to feed four pieces of unequal thickness at one time.

FEED consists of four powerfully driven rolls. All roll gears keyed to the shafts, no studs. All gears cut from the solid. Top infeeding roll in four sections. Feed controlled by tight and loose pulleys operated by a lever at the feed-in end. Feed, 20′, 24′ and 30′ per minute, or faster, if ordered.

COUNTERSHAFT has tight and loose pulleys, 12″ x 6½″, and makes 900 r. p. m. Loose pulley is our bronze bush self-oiling, non-dripping type.

EQUIPMENT: Regularly furnished with full set of knives and necessary wrenches.

No.	Size	Floor Space	H. P.	C. M.
147	24″ x 6′	5′ 10′ x 5′ 3′	25	150
147	30″ x 6′	5′ 10′ x 5′ 9′	25	160

These details are constantly subject to change as improvement directs

No. 156—Ball Bearing—Electric Precision Cabinet Smoothing Planer

DESIGN: A machine of correct design and careful construction for producing the very highest grade of work in furniture, piano, and cabinet factories, or wherever a fine smooth surface is required. Exclusive features built into this machine advance the operator in producing a continuous flow of production without a planer mark, leaving little if anything for the sander to do but polish.

CONSTRUCTION: All sizes plane 7″ thick. Frame heavy cored type, bed supported on long wedges or inclines almost the entire length of frame and adjusted by wedge platen. Four 5″ feed rolls, powerfully driven. All gears cut from the solid and entirely enclosed. Chip breaker raises concentric with head. No studs. Infeed rolls and chip breaker solid or sectional as ordered. Chip breaker raises concentric with head. Cylinder turns in four ball bearings, Three-knife full-round type with thin air-hardened Tungsten steel knives and has Setting and Jointing Device. Surfaces as short as 6″. Spring pressure system to feed rolls.

DRIVE: For alternating current 2 or 3 phase 60 cycle, 110, 220 or 440 volt motor is mounted direct on cylinder. Where A. C. is not available motor is direct coupled to cylinder; or where slower speed motor must be used we can furnish machine with motor direct geared. Motor may be coupled to countershaft for belted drive.

COUNTERSHAFT: When furnished with countershaft tight and loose pulleys are 12″ x 8″ and make 900 r. p. m.

EQUIPMENT: Regularly furnished with one set of three knives and necessary wrenches. Countershaft is included on belt drive.

No.	Size	Floor Space without C. S.	H. P.	C. M.
156	24′	4′ x 7′ 4′	10	125
156	30′	5′ 10′ x 7′ 4′	15	165
156	36′	6′ 4′ x 7′ 4′	15	190

Sectional Roll and Chipbreaker in 1″ or 3″ (extra).

These details are constantly subject to change as improvement directs

No. 502—Ball Bearing Electric Hand Planer and Jointer

Designed for general shop use—requires very little power and will do away with many hand operations and produces absolutely perfect work. A very valuable tool for any woodworking shop, large or small.

TABLES are made in two sizes, 6½" over all, and 41" over all, and 8" wide and 55" over all. They are mounted on inclines and adjust with hand wheel and screw. Fence is adjustable anywhere across the table and angles 45 degrees.

IRON PEDESTAL can be furnished on machine when so ordered.

MOTOR: As illustrated, machine may be furnished with a 3,600 r. p. m. motor mounted direct on cylinder for A. C., 2 or 3 phase, 60 cycle, 110, 220, or 440 volts. Motor may be mounted on column and belted to cylinder or bracketed to column and coupled to cylinder.

EQUIPMENT: Regularly furnished with set of three knives and necessary wrenches.

No.	Size	Floor Space without C.S.	H. P.	C. M.
502	6½"	3' 5" x 1' 6"	¾	10
502	8"	4' 7" x 1' 8"	¾	15

Aluminum Guard, (extra).

No. 502 Ball Bearing Shaftless Motor Driven Hand Planer and Jointer.

(Mounted on Pedestal)

No. 555—Ball Bearing—Electric—Portable Hand Planer and Jointer

A machine to take the place of ordinary hand planing, for jointing and fitting of pieces used in construction of patterns, cabinet work, jobbing shops, repair work, carpentry, building, manual training, and on almost all classes of work in wood construction.

The motor which is mounted self-contained on base of machine is direct coupled to cutterhead. The machine has long front table and a short rear table mounted on long inclines on base of machine with screw adjustment.

CAPACITY: Made in two widths, 4" and 6".

MOTOR: ¼ h. p., single, 2 or 3 phase, 50 and 60 cycle, 110, and 220 volt A. C., or 110 and 220 D. C., with speed of 3,600 r. p. m. Plug connector for light socket is supplied with motor.

EQUIPMENT: Regularly furnished with one set of 3 knives on the cylinder and one aluminum guard with machine. When ordering, always specify current, voltage and cycle of the electric current on which these machines are to be operated.

No.	Size	C. M.
555	4"	4
555	6"	5

Attachments (extra).
Setting, Jointing and Truing Device.
Rabbeting Arm

Rear View

19

No. 545—Ball Bearing Electric Vertical Borer
Nos. 1, 3, 190, Vertical Borers

A complete line of Borers to meet the demand for general light and heavy work in Chair, Cabinet, Vehicle, and Implement Factories, Car Shops, Arsenals, Shipyards, etc.

TYPES: No. 1 is a Single Spindle Machine, furnished regularly with one speed, 1,800 r. p. m., on special two speeds may be provided. No. 3 is a Single Spindle Automatic with 10" graduated stroke and the No. 190 has both a Vertical and a Horizontal Spindle. All machines are built on the same design with heavy one-piece column. Table 18" x 30" with Vertical, Lateral, Transverse, and Angular Adjustments of 30° either way. Spindles in heavy yoke bearings with spring counterbalance and heavy bronze socket and ball bearing thrust.

No. 545 is a direct motor driven machine with spindle running in BALL BEARINGS including a 3,600 r. p. m. motor built direct on spindle for A. C., 2 or 3 phase, 60 cycle, 110, 220, 440 volts.

Where A. C. current is not available, motor can be mounted on base (1,200 r. p. m.) and belted to pulley on spindle. Can be driven from countershaft. (1,200 r. p. m.)

EQUIPMENT: Each machine regularly furnished with one bit for each spindle, and necessary wrenches.

MOTORS: All machines may be direct coupled to 900 or 1,200 r. p. m. motors.

No.	Style	Capacity	Floor Space	H. P.	C. M.
1	One Speed	2"	2' 6" x 5' 4"	1	75
3	Graduated Stroke	2"	2' 6" x 5' 4"	2	75
190	Combination	2"	3' 3" x 4' 11"	2	75
545	Motor	2"	2' 6" x 4' 2"	5	60
545	Belt	2"	2' 6" x 5' 0"	5	75

No. 509—Ball Bearing—Electric—Sliding Head Vertical Hollow Chisel Mortiser
(Illustration shows Compound Table)

GENERAL: An advanced and exclusive model with motor on spindle, **sliding head type**, for mortising a wide range of work with extreme accuracy for automobile body and coach work, sash and door factories, manual training schools, etc.

CAPACITY: Will mortise to a depth of 3". Takes chisels ¼" to ⅝" in hard wood, up to ¾" in soft wood.

FEED: Chisel is brought down through the stock by means of treadle maintaining the table at uniform height which can be adjusted for different sizes of stock.

TABLE: Regularly furnished with plain table having vertical adjustment—compound table is extra.

DRIVES: Either with the motor mounted direct on spindle as shown for 2 or 3 phase, 60 cycle, A. C. current; or motor mounted on base, belted to pulley on spindle; or countershaft.

EQUIPMENT: Includes one chisel, any size desired within its range, with auger to suit and necessary wrenches.

No.	Drives	Floor Space	H. P.	C. M.
509	With Shaftless Motor	3' 0" x 4' 1"	3	75
509	With Countershaft	3' 9" x 4' 1"	3	75
	Compound Table (extra)			

No. 424-B—Dovetail Attachment

Dovetailing Attachments can be applied to our Single or Double Spindle Shapers. This attachment is designed for factories not having enough dovetailing to keep an independent machine constantly working. It can be put on and taken off the shaper in a very few minutes, and will take care of quite a little amount of dovetailing.

It has capacity for working material of any thickness from ¼″ up to 1½″, and of any width up to 13″, and is designed for straight front drawers.

Improved Shaper Guard

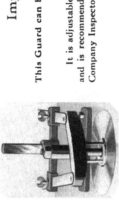

This Guard can be applied to any Shaper and will be found thoroughly effective

It is adjustable in all directions, complies with all safety laws and is recommended by State Factory and Liability Insurance Company Inspectors everywhere.

No. 498—Fluting Attachment for Friezers or Shapers

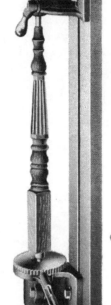

This is a very simple, yet reliable device for spacing off and fluting pillars, newel posts, balusters, table legs and work of that class.

The shape of the flute is governed by the shape of the cutter on the spindle of the machine, and the index plate spaced so as to give the desired number of flutes or beads accurately on straight or tapered stock. A suitable form is provided to give correct depth of cut making a very complete attachment to a Shaper (single or double spindle). It will take stock any diameter up to 8″.

No. 252—Ball Bearing—Single Spindle Shaper

Vertical Reversible Motor Drive

DESIGNED for general use in furniture, carriage, wagon, chair, bracket, picture frame factories, manual training schools, etc. This is the most advanced type of single shaper made—fitted with Ball Bearings and taper spindle. The spindle runs perfectly true at the highest speeds, increasing output and finishing work absolutely smooth

COLUMN is heavy, cast in one piece and cored.

TABLE is 31″ x 36″ planed and ground perfectly true and fitted with two concentric rings. It is slotted and fitted with an adjustable fence as shown.

SPINDLE is of best crucible steel, taper ground, regularly made with a solid ⅞″ stem, and takes a 4″ knife between collars, but can be arranged to use stem-chucks with various sizes of stems to suit cutters with larger bores for heavier material and the use of dovetail cutter chucks. It is fitted in a solid yoked frame which has vertical adjustment of 4″ in wide dovetail slides and has gibbed take-up for removing all lost motion.

COUNTERSHAFT: Plain countershaft or friction reverse if desired, which has tight and loose pulleys, 8″ x 4½″, 950 r. p. m. Driving pulley is 10″ x 4½″, 750 r. p. m.

MOTOR: 900-1,200 direct coupled to countershaft or 1,800 r. p. m. Vertical Motor belted direct to spindle and operated with a reversible switch as shown in the illustration.

EQUIPMENT: Regularly furnished with one reversible cutter on spindle and wrenches.

No.	Floor Space without C. S.	H. P.	C. M.
252	2′ 7″ x 3′ 0″	3	35

Dovetail chuck and spindle with extension stem (extra)

These details are constantly subject to change as improvement directs

No. 345 with motor on column, Iron Doors and Wire Mesh Guards

No. 345—Ball Bearing—36" Band Scroll Saw

COLUMN is a single cored casting with broad floor support.

TABLE is 33" x 29", made of iron, and tips to right, 45 degrees.

WHEELS are 36" diameter by 2" face. Upper wheel is steel spoke, vertically adjustable, and is supplied with our regular weighted tension. Lower wheel solid or steel spoke. Cast iron doors for lower wheel and wire mesh guard for upper wheel are provided at a slight additional cost, when so ordered. Ball Bearing Roller Saw Guides both above and below table.

COUNTERSHAFT has tight and loose pulleys, 14" x 3½", 900 r. p. m.

MOTOR 3 h. p., 1,800 r. p. m., may be belted or 900 r. p. m. coupled, or shaftless motor at 900 r. p. m. may be had.

No. 436—Resaw Attachment.

EQUIPMENT: Regularly furnished with one ⅝" saw blade ready for use, and brazing tools.

DESIGNED to meet the needs of schools and small shops for a small amount of resawing. No increase in floor space required and no parts in the way of the operator.

RESAWS 17" wide and to the center of 8' on Nos. 50 and 58 and 15" wide on No. 345. Each roll adjusts independently and can be beveled for sawing siding.

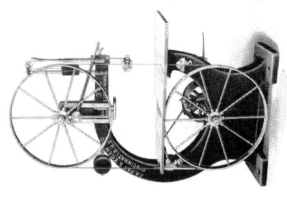

No. 345—36" Band Scroll Saw

No. 436 Resaw Attachment, as applied to our No. 345 Band Saw

No.	Size	Style	H. P.	C. M.
345	36"	Regular	3 to 5	90
		600 r. p. m. Shaftless Motor Drive		
		900 r. p. m. Shaftless Motor Drive		
436		Resaw Attachment.		5
		Guard (extra).		

No.	Style	Floor Space	H.P.	C.M.
345		4' 2" x 4' 10"		

No. 469 and 469 A—Ball Bearing—Electric—Scroll Saws

DESIGNED for use in furniture, pattern, carpenter and cabinet shops. Intricate scroll sawing, including internal and external curve work, can be handled very easily on this machine. 1½ h. p., 900 r. p. m. motor for either A. C. or D. C. mounted directly in base. Foot Lever instantly controls both electric current and brake simultaneously.

No. 469 is built with the top arm for plants that are arranged to permit suspending the strain overhead.

Regularly furnished with twelve assorted 14" saws and necessary wrenches.

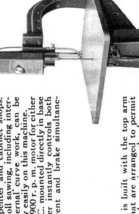

No.	Style	Floor Space	H. P.	C. M.	Belt Code	Motor
469	Without Arm	2' 9" x 3' 3"	1½	29	Gaafu	Gaagv
469-A	With Arm	2' 9" x 3' 5"	1½	51	Gaape	Gaarg
	Boring Attachment (extra).					

No. 470—Ball Bearing—Electric—Scroll Saw

In furniture, cabinet and pattern shops this machine will do all kinds of scroll sawing of the highest quality, including internal and external curve work. Especially valuable where no ceiling or wall is to be had for support.

Heavy one-piece cored casting, having broad floor supports. No vibration.

TABLE: Is made of iron, measures 39" x 33". Angles 30 degrees to right and to left, and can be securely locked at any angle by means of a quick acting lever.

TENSION: Is the most flexible ever put on a scroll saw and is entirely enclosed in an aluminum case.

MOTOR DRIVE: 1½ h. p. 900 r. p. m. motor for alternating or direct current is mounted directly on base. Foot lever which is at operator's convenience automatically cuts off current and at the same time serves as a brake for stopping machine instantly—leaving operators both hands free for the work.

EQUIPMENT: Regularly furnished with twelve assorted 14" saws and necessary wrenches.

No.	Style	Floor Space	H.P.	C.M.
470	Pulleys on Flywheel Shaft	3' 3" x 4' 11"	1½	75
470	Motor on Flywheel Shaft	3' 3" x 4' 11"	1½	75
	Boring Attachment (extra).			

No. 500—Ball Bearing—Electric—Variety Saw

SAFETY FIRST: Saw blade runs in a cast iron chute with removable cover, and can have our aluminum guard above. No chance for an accident. This chute also removes the sawdust either to an exhaust or to a box if you have no exhaust. A valuable safety feature is our aluminum splitter guard which spreads the stock, preventing binding, pinching or kicking back, which can be applied at small extra cost.

FRAME: Column is a heavy one-piece casting carrying motor, table and table yoke, this being mounted in gibbed ways.

TABLE: Table is 38″ x 44″ and is a heavy ribbed casting, mounted on machined segments. It angles up to 45° by hand-wheel and screw, having a brass index plate to show the exact angle. Table has vertical adjustment of 5″. Both adjustments are self-locking in any position. There is no back-breaking strain required to raise table, the ball bearings on raising screw making it very easy. On special order we can equip the No. 500 with a sliding table as shown on page 141: front half of table which is 18″ wide is mounted on ball bearings and has a movement of 33″ for edging and cutting off up to 30″ wide. This machine is made in three types. No. 500 having a table 38″ x 44″, No. 500-C having a table 27″ x 30″ and No. 500-F having a sliding table 38″ x 44″.

DRIVING ARRANGEMENT: Special 5 h. p., 3,600 r. p. m. motor, self-ventilating, alternating current only for two or three phase, 110-220-440 volts; 60 cycle, mounted solidly on top of column, the rotor being secured directly to mandrel. Ball bearings make it easy running and prevent all end motion, controlled by switch.

FENCES: Machine is furnished without fences and the purchaser has the selection of the following fences which can be furnished at extra cost; double face rip fence, two miter fences with connecting yokes, adjustable bevel rip fence, bevel rip fence with micrometer adjustment.

MORTISING AND BORING ATTACHMENT: On special order we can equip this saw with Boring Attachment or Hollow Chisel Mortising and Boring Attachment. The mortiser can be used while the saw is in use without any interference. It mortises rapidly and accurately without pounding or jarring. Each mortise is perfect with square corners and sharp edges. No chips left to be picked out by hand. Uses mortiser chisels from ¼″ to ¾″, any length of mortise up to 3″ deep. Table is 19″ x 10″, mounted on heavy cast-iron bracket which permits of vertical adjustment of 8″. Table moves laterally 5″ on dovetail ways by means of foot treadle and iron links (no ropes or chains to break), has stop for regulating depth of mortise or boring. Fence is adjustable in "T" slots. Stationary fence is provided to hold stock when withdrawn from cut. Chisel is carried in a cast-iron holder and is easily changed.

EQUIPMENT: When regularly furnishing this machine, one 14″ rip-saw and one 14″ cross-cut saw are included. When mortising attachment is desired, one ½″ Hollow Chisel and Auger to suit is included. When boring attachment is desired, one ½″ or ⅝″ boring bit is furnished.

No.	Table	Floor Space	H. P.	C. M.
500	38″ x 44″	3′ 2″ x 3′ 11″	5	50
500-C	27″ x 30″	2′ 5″ x 2′ 9″	5	45
500-F	38″ x 44″	3′ 0″ x 6′ 5″	5	50

ATTACHMENTS (extra)

Boring Attachment.................................
Hollow Chisel Mortising and Boring Attachment.......
Aluminum Saw Guard...............................
Universal Saw Guard..............................

These details are constantly subject to change us improvement directs

No. 500—Ball Bearing—Electric—Variety Saw

1. Motor mounted directly on column, impossible to get out of line. Rotor direct on Arbor.
2. Table can be tilted to any angle up to 45 degrees.
3. No countershaft required.
4. No belts.
5. Arbor runs in Self-Aligning Ball Bearings.
6. Stopped and started by totally enclosed fused switch.

DESIGNED for use in carpenter and variety shops, furniture, carriage, automobile body and agricultural implement factories, technical and manual training schools. It is the embodiment of the highest degree of engineering skill devoted to building into every unit the last ounce of saw power. This is the latest development in the saw line for variety cutting, grooving, gaining, etc.

CAPACITY: Regular machine with table 38″ x 44″ with a 14″ blade will rip stock up to 3″ thick, 24″ to right and 16″ to left, or will cut-off stock up to 1″ thick and 18″ wide. If small table (27″ x 30″) is preferred, blade will cut 14½″ to right and 11″ to left and will cut-off up to 12″ wide.

23

No. 402—Ball Bearing—Universal Saw Bench

DESIGNED for ripping and cross-cutting in cabinet, pattern, sash and door shops, etc., especially adapted for use in manual training schools and technical colleges. Its application is almost unlimited. It has a wide range of adjustments, all quickly made, and will meet all the requirements where a medium priced tool is wanted. Rips 14" between saw and fence and through material 3½" thick. Made in two styles: No. 402-A, with fence equipment as shown above, and No. 402-B, with ripping fence, having micrometer adjustment, miter cut-off fence with extension stop rod, clearance block, table grooved for cut-off fences and provided with filler strips. As regularly furnished machine should be belted from below; idlers for belting from countershaft on same floor, or machine arranged for self-contained motor drive furnished when ordered. Motor should be 5 horsepower, 1,800 r. p. m.

Table measures 44" x 37" and angles to 45 degrees by means of hand wheel and screw; self-locking in any position. Made in two sections, the left hand section 17" wide and traveling on frictionless rollers. Table opens up to permit the use of grooving heads on the mandrels. Two graduated quadrants are inscribed in the traveling table, each having an adjustable fence by means of which right and left angles can be cut without readjustment.

GUARDS: Machine regularly furnished with door over opening in frame, making saw blade easily accessible and at the same time completely closing it. Splitters to travel with the saw blades furnished without extra charge, if wanted. Universal adjustable aluminum saw guard to cover blade above table furnished if ordered.

COUNTERSHAFT: Regularly furnished with one 14" rip and one 14" cross-cut saw and necessary wrenches.

EQUIPMENT: Regularly furnished with tight and loose pulleys, 10" x 5½", 600 r. p. m.

No.	Table	Floor Space	H.P.	C.M.
402-A	44" x 36½"	3'1" x 3'8"	5	74
402-B	44" x 36½"	3'1" x 3'8"	5	74
Idlers (extra).				

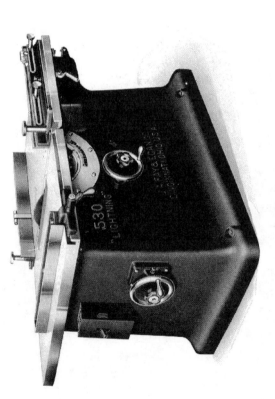

No. 530—Ball Bearing—Electric—Mitering, Beveling, and Dadoing Machine

Will cut any compound angle up to 45 degrees with table same height and position. Will dado up to 2" wide, 1" deep.

GENERAL: A single combination unit that will produce with extreme accuracy mitering and beveling, ripping, cross-cutting, dadoing, etc. Rigidly constructed to insure against operating strain under severe conditions. Just the machine where the schedule calls for intensive production in coach and body factories, planing mills, casket factories, sash and door plants, etc.

CAPACITY: Will cut-off 30" wide, 1" thick, or 27" wide, 4⅛" thick, with a 16" saw. When arbor is angled at 45 degrees, will cut through stock 3" thick. Will dado up to 2" wide, 1" deep, with 10" head. Will rip up to 32" wide, to the right of saw, and 23" wide to left of saw when using double face rip fence.

TABLES: Left hand table 26" x 40", heavily ribbed with slide at front for double face rip fence. Right hand table 35" x 40" and travels on balls. This table may be locked in alignment with stationary table by lever at front making one large ripping table 61" x 40".

ANGLING ARBOR UNIT: Including the motor which is built direct on the angling arbor and saw as a complete unit angle up to 45°. The pivot point being at the intersection of the tables and saw line eliminates the need for any vertical adjustment after angling the arbor. Index conveniently placed shows the angle of arbor from vertical to 45°.

DRIVES: For A. C. current, 2 or 3 phase, 60 cycle, 110, 220, or 440 volts, motor is mounted direct on the arbor. Where A. C. current is not available a 1,200 r. p. m. motor can be coupled to the countershaft. For lineshaft drive, tight and loose pulleys are furnished on the countershaft.

COUNTERSHAFT: A cast connected hanger carries a drum pulley, fiber gravity idler pulley, and with tight and loose pulleys, 8" x 9½" and should make 1,200 r. p. m.

EQUIPMENT: Regularly furnished with one 16" combination rip and cross-cut saw blade, double face rip fence for use on either side of table, right and left mitering fences on either side of traveling table. Graduations are cut in the table top for lining up fences to 45°. A hinged movable stop dog is provided on each. A swivel miter fence having dovetail slide in stationary table is also furnished.

No.	Drive	Floor Space	H.P.	C.M.
530	Motor on Arbor	5'1" x 3'4"	5	50
530	Belt Drive	5'8" x 5'4"	5	60
Guard (extra).				

No. 283

No. 223–A with "V" Table

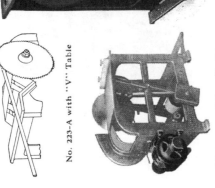

Motor mounted on Frame

No. 223—Inverted Swing Cut-Off Saw

DESIGNED for the rapid cutting off of light material, such as required in the manufacture of cabinets, sash and doors, etc. It will be found very valuable in any shop.

CAPACITY: Will cut off material 1″ thick up to 20″ wide, or 4″ thick by 8″ wide with regular 16″ saw. A 20″ saw will cut off 6″ thick by 10″ wide.

SAW ARBOR is mounted on a swinging frame with bearings in the base of the frame. It is operated by foot lever shown in cut, and is provided with our special counteracting lever, insuring an easy movement forward and a quick return. An adjustable stop rod with collars is provided to enable the operator to make the stroke of the saw short or long as his work requires. The collars are cushioned to prevent any jar on return movement of saw. Automatic tighteners keep belt properly tensioned.

Machine may be arranged with table made with a "V" cross top 5″ deep for cutting off cord wood. By means of this "V" and the hold-down it is possible to hold these awkwardly shaped pieces firmly, greatly increasing the amount of work and preventing accidents caused by pieces being thrown about by saw as often happens where this work is done on a regular table, 26″ blade furnished.

No. 283: Same machine with table on both sides of saw, designated No. 283.

COUNTERSHAFT is mounted in bearings in the frame and has tight and loose pulleys, 8″ x 5½″, 750 r. p. m.

MOTOR, 5 h. p., 1,800 r. p. m., mounted, self-contained.

EQUIPMENT: Regularly furnished with one 16″ cut-off saw and necessary wrenches.

No.	Size	Floor Space	H. P.	C. M.
223	16′	3′ 2″ x 4′ 1″	5	50
283	16′	4′ 6″ x 5′ 6″	5	80
"V" Table				

700 without the Angling Device

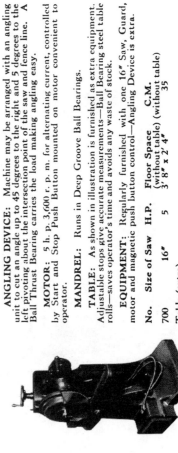

No. 700—Electric—Ball Bearing—Straight Line Cut-Off Saw
(With Angling Device)

For greater efficiency in the cutting room the "700" Straight Line Cut-Off Saw deserves your consideration. Quicker in movement, surpassingly swift and easy in operation, each movement floating on Ball or Roller Bearings. Being a motorized, self contained floor unit it can be placed in any convenient place and as there are no projections for interference, can be placed flush against the wall occupying very little floor space.

CAPACITY: On a straight line it will cut through stock 20″ wide and 1″ thick or 17″ wide and 4″ thick with 16″ saw.

ANGLING DEVICE: Machine may be arranged with an angling unit to cut an angle up to 45 degrees to the right and 5 degrees to the left pivoting about the intersection point of the saw and fence line. A Ball Thrust Bearing carries the load making angling easy.

MOTOR: 5 h. p. 3,600 r. p. m. for alternating current, controlled by Start and Stop Push Button and magnetic push button control. Angling Device is extra.

MANDREL: Runs in Deep Groove Ball Bearings.

TABLE: As shown in illustration is furnished as extra equipment. Adjustable stops give accurate measurements—Ball Bearing steel table rolls—saves operator's time and avoids any waste of stock.

EQUIPMENT: Regularly furnished with one 16″ Saw, Guard, motor and magnetic push button control—Angling Device is extra.

No.	Size of Saw	H.P.	Floor Space (without table)	C.M. (without table)
700	16″	5	3′ 8″ x 2′ 4″	35

Table (extra).

Angling Device (extra).

25

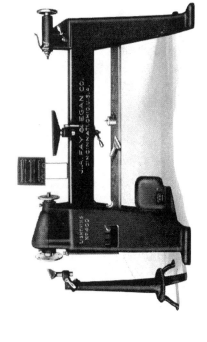

No. 400-A

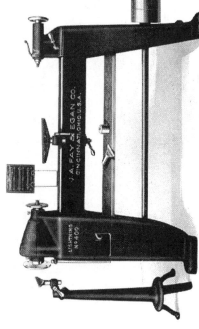

No. 400-B

No. 400-C

No. 400-D

No. 400 — Manual Training Lathes
Multi-Speed Motor Headstock

These lathes are designed for use in manual training schools and colleges, and are absolutely fool-proof. They can be operated by the most inexperienced and careless student without danger of injuring the machine or the operator. They are from 300 to 500 pounds heavier than any other manual training lathes made.

No. 400 TYPE A is made with variable speed motor head stock, available for use on direct current only. Motor is a ½ h. p., 750–3,000 r. p. m. totally enclosed. The controlling apparatus is built in and also totally enclosed, giving 24 speeds, by means of hand wheel. In addition to the feed control, each starter is provided with time limit thermal relays and starting resistance.

No. 400 TYPE D LATHE is made with variable speed motor, ball bearing headstock for use on alternating current only. Motor is ½ h. p., totally enclosed, having 4 speeds, 550, 1,140, 1,720 and 3,400. Controlling apparatus is drum type and is built in, operating very easily but preventing sudden throw from low to high speed.

CAPACITIES: All styles made 12″ swing and standard bed is 4′ long and 24″ between centers, but can be extended to any length required. All spindles regularly threaded on both ends. Outside floor stand and rest can be used with any machine and is furnished as additional equipment when ordered. Hand Feed Carriage with plain or compound swivel rest, set over tail stock and other special lathe equipment can be applied to either type.

Although designed primarily for manual training work, these lathes have been adopted by many large manufacturers who recognized in them a speed lathe of superior merit in every respect. Interested parties are invited to write for large special bulletin, illustrating and describing these machines in detail.

No.	Swing	Distance Between Centers
400-A	12″	24″
400-D	12″	24″

No. 400 — Manual Training Lathes
Ball Bearing Headstock

No. 400 TYPE B is for use on an alternating current, either single, two, or three phase, any cycle or voltage, and also for d. c. and has a ½ h. p. constant speed motor mounted in the base of the machine. Belt driven to the head stock spindle, giving four speeds. All operating apparatus is totally enclosed, and the stopping, starting and speed changes are accomplished by means of the one handle control.

No. 400 TYPE C is similar to the B Type, except it is intended for use where power is taken from a line shaft or to be connected up in series, having a number of lathes driven by one motor, and for this purpose having a drive shaft self-contained, mounted in base, with adjustable bearings and enclosed in hollow tubing.

No.	Swing	Distance Between Centers
400-B	12″	24″
400-C	12″	24″

Chapter 2

THE YATES-AMERICAN MACHINE COMPANY

"Berlin Quality"

In October 1876, workmen/inventors J.L. Perry and Almon Bridgman of Berlin, Wisconsin, set up and put into operation their prototype thickness sander at their employer's factory, The Berlin Coffin and Casket Manufacturing Company. Then popularly called a "wood-polishing" or "sand-papering" machine, the concept was something new.

Resembling a planer, it consisted of a heavy oak table with a series of spring-loaded feed rolls above. Protruding through a slot in the table was a large wooden cylinder covered first with rubber and then with sandpaper. The rollers slowly fed the stock through the machine and over the high speed sanding head, "polishing" the underside smooth and level, ready for varnishing. At 15 feet per minute the machine did in one day what it took 100 man hours to do – namely, prepare materials for 100 coffins – and did it better.

In April 1877 Perry and Bridgman received their patent and in 1878 began manufacturing and selling their new sander, which they proudly christened "The Boss Wood Polisher." By May 1879, after less than a year of operation, they had sold over 100 machines.

Davis, Pugh & Co. (which originally made the sanders to order) consisted, in 1878, of a foundry, a machine shop, and a blacksmithing shop, employing 12 to 15 first class mechanics. By 1880 the company was manufacturing twin and triple drum power feed sanders. In October 1881 J.L. Perry & Co. (Bridgman had since sold out) purchased controlling interest in Davis, Pugh and began increasing sander production capabilities.

A picture of the prototype "Boss" Wood Polisher has yet to appear, nor has an early commercial model. However, a fine engraving of the redesigned machine appears in the 1888 woodworking machinery catalog of The Hoyt & Brother Company of Aurora, Illinois (see p. 34).

By October 1883, what were now the J.L. Perry & Co. shops were among the best in the state. The company employed between 60 and 70 men. It was its intention to build other woodworking machines besides the sanders, which were being offered in single and double cylinder models.

One such machine was the "Economist," a two-drum oscillating thickness sander, patented March 6, 1883. The drums were 12" in diameter. Not only were *they* of wood but so were the gibs that secured the paper. The sander was equipped with two iron feed rolls up and down and a revolving brush to remove dust.

The company also manufactured the "Avalanche", a new planer and smoother, and a spindle machine for sanding moldings, blind slats, ornamental work, etc.

In December 1883 the firm of J.L. Perry & Co. was dissolved and Perry's interests were purchased by a Mr. Mather, who became sole owner of the newly renamed Berlin Machine Works. Mather intended to increase sales and upgrade the facility as needed.

However, Mather soon sold the business to a Mr. Van Dyke of Milwaukee who, in turn, sold the Works to Joseph and Porter B. Yates, who took possession of the firm and all its patents on September 24, 1884. [There is a single, very brief and unsubstantiated, account of P.B. Yates manufacturing a rival sanding machine, but the author can find nothing more about it – perhaps a reader can shed some light on it.]

Yates was born in Schenectady, New York, in 1854. He came from a long line of Mohawk Dutch, the original settlers of New York's Mohawk Valley. In the spring of 1855 his father, Joseph Yates, traveled to Berlin, Wisconsin, where he and his brother-in-law, John D. Porter, opened the city's first hardware store. The family followed in 1857. Young Porter attended local schools and worked for a time in the family business before he bought the sander company.

Porter began expanding the business. By 1886 over 1500 of the "Economist" sander-planers were in use in the largest woodworking factories all over the world. It was calculated that the heavy-duty machine did the work of 20 men and produced a finish surpassing hand-surfacing. The sander-planer had extensive sales in large furniture factories and was especially adapted for any factory having sectional work. In fact, the Berlin Machine Works was the only company in the United States that specialized in building sanders.

On August 5, 1886, *The Berlin Weekly Journal* reported the shops of the Works were to be overhauled in the Fall. Among the improvements: new floors would be laid through the entire building, more power would be run in and electric lighting installed. It would be necessary to operate the Works night and day during the next winter to fill orders.

On September 10, 1886, Yates invited all the businessmen of Berlin to come to the Works and see the newly installed Edison electric light plant in operation from 7:30 to 8:00 p.m. Yates hoped to interest them in organizing a plant for business lighting in the city itself.

In 1887 the Works constantly employed 75 men, but at times this number would double, with work shifts running night and day to fill orders. The company was incorporated under state laws during 1887, and a number of machines were shipped to England to be shown at the American Exhibition.

Yates needed a larger labor market, a greater power source, and a larger facility; in 1888 the company moved to nearby Beloit, Wisconsin. Under Yates's leadership the work force would grow to almost 1000 and the line greatly expand. For many years the company was the second largest employer in the area. The machines were much in demand by lumber mills, furniture factories, and schools, not only nationally but internationally, because of the strict quality control imposed by Yates. He demanded and got near perfection in every machine that left his factory.

The company prospered and expanded. In its heyday it supported a famous saxophone band, organized the Little League and the Boys' Baseball Program, fostered the Boys' Club, and held huge annual picnics.

By 1888 the Works had introduced its famous "Invincible" sander (see p. 36). This was another licensed machine built and marketed by Hoyt & Brother and listed in its 1888 catalog.

In early 1893 the company employed some 250 hands, a 100% increase over the 1892 workforce.

In 1908 Yates completed a large factory in Hamilton (Ontario, Canada) and began manufacturing woodworking machinery using the city's hydroelectricity.

In April 1909 the publicity department of the Works began publishing a small journal called *Berlin Quality,* priced at 24¢ a year. The April 1913 issue discussed the merits of various machines.

In 1916, because of public aversion to anything remotely German, Yates changed the name of the company from The Berlin Machine Works to the P.B. Yates Machine Company, both in the United States and Canada.

Catalog Number 14, circa 1917, lists some 72 basic machine models. Such options as square or round cutterheads, flat belt or motor drive, and size, increased the permutations to well over 200. With the exception of the N-1 Shaper, the Type

V-40 Tilting Band Saw, and the Type S-2 Edge Sander, all machines were equipped with babbitt bearings.

Yates also carried three models of log carriages, seven grinder models, surfacing heads, side heads, profile heads, milled-to-pattern bits, etc. The Royal Invincible Sander, the No. 87 Matcher, the No. 290 Picket Head, and the No. 302 Band Mill mentioned in 1913 do not appear.

The catalog boldly billed the company as "The Largest Manufacturer of Woodworking Machinery in the World" – a claim also made by the J.A. Fay & Egan Company.

A typical example of Yates's machine designing and craftsmanship was its No. 199 Hand Planer (Jointer) shown on p. 42. Seven feet long, it was offered for sale as early as 1913. The machine was primarily intended for small planing mills, vocational schools, pattern shops, etc., whose volume of work did not justify the purchase of the Yates No. 213 Continuous Feed Glue Jointer (p. 43).

A circa 1918 sectional catalog of woodworking machinery stated that the Yates plants at Beloit and Hamilton, combined, covered 42 acres, with a total floor area of 760,000 sq.ft. and had issued $2,500,000 in paid capital stock. The catalog had three machines not seen in Catalog No.14 – the 19½" x 7½" Type P-1 Sizer, the No.472 Automatic Feeding Table, and the No.137 Side and Profile Grinder.

During the first two and a half decades of the 20th century, Yates was truly a giant enterprise. The company made breaking down machinery (the process of converting logs into lumber), as well as woodworking machinery for further processing of the rough sawn lumber and the manufacturing of finished products. Yates could equip a complete mill: lineshafting, power transmission gear (pulleys, belting, etc.), handling equipment, woodworking machinery, maintenance equipment, etc. The equipment needed to outfit a mill could be immense. An old photograph shows a long freight train loaded with nothing but Yates woodworking machinery bound for a railroad shop where raw logs straight from the woods went in one end and emerged at the other as finished freight and passenger cars.

An instruction book for Yates Roll-Fed Sanders (1923) sheds some light on how machines were numbered and the company's repair parts policy. To aid in ordering replacement parts, each casting, forging, etc., bore a symbol number – either cast directly into it or stamped on a machined surface. Serial numbers were usually carried on a small cast iron plate with raised figures, bolted to the machine in some conspicuous place. "In recent years," states the book, "Yates serial numbers have been in five figures. There are no letters attached. Very old Yates machines sometimes will be found with four-figure serial numbers."

In 1925 Yates Machine acquired one of its largest competitors, The American Wood Working Machinery Company of Rochester, New York, a company that had itself absorbed several competitors over the years. Out of the merger arose the Yates-American Machine Co., with factories in Beloit, Rochester, and Hamilton.

The first combined catalog of this new company contained over 300 machines and the company claimed it was the largest woodworking machinery manufacturer in the world. The catalog contained a combination of modern machines, such as ball bearing electric molders, and antiquated belt-driven, babbitt-bearing machines, such as tablesaws with wooden frames and tables of glued-up wooden strips. The wide range of machinery offered by Yates-American ruled out mass production and most machines were probably made to order.

American's Clement "Perfection" Jointers and Buzz Planers for example, built in 8, 12, 16, 20, 24, and 30 inch widths (with over 3000 in use by 1903), became the Yates-American No.1 Hand Jointers.

Catalog 25-S (1930), published by the Vocational Division of Yates-American, illustrated just how strong a force the company had become in the market place. Yates-American had become the exclusive representative of the vocational woodworking machinery built by Baxter D. Whitney & Son of Winchendon, Massachusetts, Jenkins Machine Co. of Sheboygan Falls, Wisconsin, and the L.G. McKnight & Son Co. of Gardner, Massachusetts.

One highly unusual machine in the Yates-American vocational line was the Type Y-5 Open-Side Band Saw. A novel departure in frame design, the Y-5 was the only bandsaw that could actually cut squarely across boards of any length up to 18 inches wide. The cast iron saw, weighing some 750 pounds, was designed with five wheels instead of two, the blade being made to travel in two planes, one at right angles to the other. The wheels set in the corner of the frame were mounted at an angle, acting as corner idler pulleys. Stock up to 8" could be cut with the guard in place and in cutting a scroll design a clearance of 36" could be obtained. The 20" x 22" table would tilt 45° right. The saw used blades 15'4" long.

A machine of 1934 vintage was the 14" G-87 Tilting Arbor Variety Saw. The two-blade, double arbor, direct motor driven tablesaw had been designed primarily for use in schools and small shops but could hold its own in the production of small parts. It was built on a rigid, one-piece box type cast iron frame that assured accuracy and permanency. The table was a heavy, ribbed casting carefully machined true. A cross-cut blade could be placed on one end of the arbor and a rip blade on the other and rotated into position as needed by a hand wheel.

A full page ad printed in the September-October 1935 issue of *Popular Homecraft* revealed that Yates-American was entering a new market to offset the reduction in sales due to the depression: "Woodworking Machines for the Home Shop, the School Shop, the Industrial Shop by the World's Largest Manufacturer of Woodworking Machinery Will Be Announced Soon."

As promised in the September-October issue, the December issue carried four full page ads revealing an "addition to its line of heavy machines which have been serving industry for over 50 years," – the new 1936 W-Line.

By 1937, Yates-American had added the W-110 shaper and the W-75 12" jigsaw to complete the line. The shaper had a spindle speed of 8,000-10,000 rpm. Painted a flecked green, all the machines were ball bearing, with enclosed drives, and heavy duty construction (ribbed cast iron).

An April-May 1937 a *Popular Homecraft* ad described the W-30 drill press. It had "Multispeed Drive" which provided finger-tip speed control without touching a belt or moving the motor. A built-in spindle lock held the spindle securely while opening and closing the chuck. The drill head was supported on two heavy, cold drawn, seamless steel tubes. All driving and operating mechanisms were enclosed to protect operator and machine. The tilting, heavily ribbed table was nickel-alloy cast iron. The drill press was available in bench and floor models.

By 1936, manufacturing operations had been limited to Beloit and Hamilton. However, the company still maintained the Rochester plant to handle any possible future overflow from the Beloit facility, whose entire floor space was in use by a workforce of 500. The complete line of woodworking machinery being built included more than 200 machines. The largest was a heavy duty fast feed planer and matcher which weighed 37,000 pounds and was 18' long and 8' wide. The machine was designed to produce 600 feet of finished boards a minute, such as flooring and siding, from rough stock. It would mill all four sides at one pass.

However, to maintain a steady cash flow, Yates-American no longer restricted itself to woodworking machinery. New products were developed, such as car radiators, condensers and evaporators for refrigeration systems, and industrial radiators for heavy duty gasoline and Diesel engines.

In 1939, Yates-American was one of the world's three largest manufacturers of woodworking machinery, a title shared with Thomas Robinson & Sons, Rochdale, England and the Guilliet Co., Auxerre, France.

A quick look at various sources gives a general outline of what machines became available over the next few years: the No.20 Universal (two arbor) tablesaw with tilting top and sliding table (1928); the No.1 Variety Saw with mortising attachment and tilting top; the No.2 Double Cut-Off Saw; the No.287 Chain Feed Horizontal Bandsaw; the No.7 Disk and Spindle Sander, and the No.S23 three-drum thickness sander (all 1937); the J-20 Variety Saw with tilting arbor (1938); and the G-87 Variety Saw with tilting arbor (1940).

In 1950 Yates-American employed about 1500 people, with about 500 engaged in making woodworking machinery – moulders, matchers, band resaws, band mills, etc. It maintained its own foundry and built its own electric motors. It no longer sold other companies' machinery.

Yates-American had another brief flirtation with the home workshop market in the 1950s. It began manufacturing the J-Line, a hobby oriented selection of light-duty woodworking machinery, but faced tough competition from such firms as Walker-Turner Co., Boice-Crane Co., Atlas Press Co., and Rockwell.

Industrial Arts and Vocational Education in January 1951, carried one of the cleverest adverising gimmicks ever used to sell woodworking machinery. "Guesswork's gone from school shop planning," says the ad, "when you use these new models of Yates-American's popular J-Line machines. Every machine in the line is accurately reproduced – ½ inch to the foot – to enable you to check your projected arrangements on a similarly scaled drawing. That means you can be sure your layout will provide the greatest possible convenience, safety and space economy." The miniatures could either be purchased or borrowed for 60 days.

Apparently the new line was not a success. Stephen Rose, retired industrial arts instructor, wrote to the author: "Yates-American made both light and heavy duty equipment. I liked their heavy equipment, but I had very little respect for the lighter machines when they ventured into that field."

A new planer, the B-244, was introduced in 1950. The machine featured a variable feed (25 to 70 fpm), a four-knife cutterhead, and ball bearings.

The 24" surfacer had a capacity of ⅛" to 8". By the late 1950s Yates-American was making a modern wide belt thickness sander.

Around 1961, Rockwell (Delta) purchased the rights to the J-180 18 x 6 planer from Yates-American. The company manufactured the two-speed, direct drive planer for Rockwell temporarily, until the tooling could be transferred to its Bellefontaine, Ohio, facilities. Although this planer is no longer listed, as of 1983 most parts were still available through Delta's Memphis, Tennessee, distribution center.

Yates-American eventually sold the rest of the J-Line to one of its major distributors, Brodhead-Garrett Company of Cleveland, Ohio, whose 1955-56 catalog carried Yates-American machines with steep prices.

In 1961 Yates-American purchased the S.A. Woods Machine Company (est. 1854) and moved from its quarters in Beloit to Roscoe, Illinois, about 5 miles south. Twenty years later (1981), the company moved back to Beloit and to its present location in the industrial park.

In 1981 Yates-American vice-president Darrell Borghi granted an extensive interview to *The Beloit Daily News*. The recession gripping the country then, and the decline in the housing industry, had taken their toll on the once-productive company, even though Borghi held that Yates-American machines had become the "Cadillac of the industry."

"We are currently building no machines in the shop," he admitted. "This may be the first time in the 98-year history of the company that this has happened. It is unprecedented bad times. We are in a very depressed state."

In the 1970s Yates-American had employed about 40 people, 18 in the shop when the plant was operating wide open – a sad total when compared to the 2000 or more work force of years before. At the time of the 1901 interview with Borghi, there were only eight people working in the shop.

Yates-American by this time was specializing in planers and matchers. According to Borghi, its matchers were the "cat's meow" in the field. But lumber mills are dependent on the housing industry and Yates-American was dependent on lumber mills.

"Yates didn't do real well until after WW II," stated Borghi. "Then it tapered off, and we've had our peaks and valleys ever since. We don't have a real good year unless interest rates are down to the 14 or 15 percent range. But you just have to maintain a healthy attitude through all this."

Yates-American, according to Borghi, stood in an unusual position. In its case it was not cheaper to manufacture fabricated steel machines, though it was more expensive to begin manufacturing cast machines. "We have the patterns from our machines. If we had to start all over we would have to make fabricated steel machines."

Borghi credited the longevity of Yates-American machines to the fact that they were made of cast iron rather than fabricated steel. "Steel fabricated parts are only as strong as the weakest weld. Cast iron also reduces friction. You can take a nickel, balance it on its side on the running motor of our deluxe planer, and it won't fall over."

Director of sales and engineering, Jerry Toppen, noted in the same interview that cast iron does not expand and contract as easily as fabricated steel. "That's important, because for a planer the determining factor of quality is the size of the finished product." Toppen proudly stated that Yates-American machines could finish a product within .0004" of specifications.

The Beloit site is still used mainly for the storage of thousands of patterns vital for making cast iron parts and the assembly of machines. Yates-American has stopped making its own machine parts (usually a sign of a company's decline). Shops in neighboring towns (which also have patterns in storage) see to the company's needs. The company carries over 15,000 service parts and has blueprints for over 300,000! Servicing certain old machines is what keeps the plant alive.

In 1989, Yates-American conducted a comprehensive review of its entire past product lines. Its study led to the company's conclusion that because of age, current state of the art design, and resultant safety considerations hundreds of its machines were now obsolete and should be taken out of service immediately. A lengthy list in the November 1989 issue of *Industrial Education* named machines that could not or would not be serviced in any respect by the Yates-American Machine Co. Among the many machines were all American, Mershon, Berlin, P.B. Yates, M-Line, W-Line, and most of the S.A. Woods brands.

To meet the increasing demand for log cabin construction the company had developed a profile tooling package to produce log cabin timbers on the A-20 and A-62 Planer-Matchers which were two of the few machines still being made to handle 8" timbers.

The B-26 Double Rough Surfacer was a typical modern Yates-American machine. Designed new from the ground up, it was almost totally made with stress-relieved steel parts. The single-piece base and removable stand components made it durable and easy to maintain. Also, because the machine was designed to use many off-the-shelf components, it could be serviced more quickly through local suppliers. Even the fork lift points were designed into the base to make transporting and positioning the machine easier.

Standard features included "Posi-Tensioning" on the infeed rolls to provide independent and variable feed pressure to yield to lumber contours no matter the species being worked, quick stopping cutterhead brakes, swiveling pendant control panel, close coupled feed roll configurations (even 4-foot boards could be self fed with jamming), flat profile urethane-filled tires to permit positive feeding of narrow stock, large 8" cutting circle cylinder head (10 spiral rows of teeth or 12 straight knives could be chosen), and an automatic air release chipbreaker.

In 1994 a combined six in-plant staff (not including field service representatives) was responsible for an ongoing customer service program to provide repair parts and support for both machines and cutting equipment in the field. As part of its commitment, Yates-American maintained a field warehouse in High Point, North Carolina, dedicated exclusively to the distribution of repair parts and tooling to the Southern and Eastern cities of the U.S. An extensive inventory of repair parts was also maintained at the Beloit facility to service the more than 200 different models of machines once or currently manufactured by the company. Both maintain a 24-hour repair parts shipment program for emergencies.

The company is still located at 2880 Kennedy Drive, Beloit, Wisconsin 53511.

The "Boss" Sandpapering Machine.

Hoyt and Brother Company Catalog 1888 - see next page

The "Boss" Sandpapering Machine

The cut on opposite page illustrates the Double Cylinder Machine as now being built by, us from patterns new and entirely remodeled. A few of the important points of excellence claimed for this Machine, and which are secured by letters patent' are as follows:

First.—The Brush Cylinder, over which the lumber passes after leaving the Sand Cylinders, which not only removes every atom of sand or loose fibre, but gives a glossy polish to the surface, result obtained by no other Machine on the market.

Second. The arrangement of Feed Rollers, raised and lowered in perfect line by means of Pitch Chain, all operated by one Hand Wheel

Third. The adjustment of Pressure Rollers of Sand Cylinders, by means of which the cut of and paper can be made light or heavy, at the will of the operator.

Fourth. The Cylinders.

Fifth.- The Self-Adjusting, Feed Rollers, which relieve all the friction of stock: from the bed, and secure the most positive feed of any Machine on the market.

Sixth.—The entire combination of parts, the result of years of careful experiments, which have happily been attended with great success, and gained for the Machine an acknowledged preeminence.

No well-appointed furniture factory, or factory in which work of a like character is being done, can now afford to be without one of these Machines. For curved surfaces, such as sides of certain patterns of burial cases, the proper Machine will be the Single Cylinder, and those desiring a Machine for coffin-work should so state when ordering For large furniture, carriage, wagon and agricultural implement factories, the Double Machine will be preferred, being, of greater capacity, although more suitable for the polishing of flat surfaces only.

Size.	Width of Stock Worked.	Thickness of Stock Worked.	Feed per Hour.	Tight and Loose Pulleys.	Shipping Weight.
No. 5 - 24 inch.	24 inches.	0 to 4 1/2 inches.	960	7 1/2 x 12	2,450 pounds.
No. 6 - 30 inch.	30 inches.	0 to 4 1/2 inches.	960	8 1/2 x 12	2,900 pounds.
No. 7 - 36 inch.	36 inches.	0 to 4 1/2 inches.	960	8 1/2 x 13	3,350 pounds.
No. 8 - 40 inch.	40 inches.	0 to 4 1/2 inches.	960	8 1/2 x 13	3,500 pounds.

The cut represents our late improved ' Boss." It is the only Sander in existence possessing the vital principle necessary to the successful workings of a Machine for polishing fine work, to-wit: The lower train of Feeding Rolls, which in any Sanding Machine virtually constitute its true bed, are hung in swinging, Bearings. These Bearings are attached to weighted Levers, as shown in cut, which move them up or down automatically, dependin, entirely upon the pressure put upon the lumber by means of the Hand Wheels which operate the Pressure Rolls. This can easily be understood when it is remembered that the mechanism mentioned above allows the lower Feed Rolls to drop below the periphery of the Sand Cylinders as far as is necessary to give the cut desired. By the use of this mechanism the " Boss', will clean the thinnest veneers without cutting through. In all other Sanders the lower Feed Rolls are stationary in the bed.

Our Brush is the only practical one used, from the fact that it is so mounted on a Cylinder by itself that it can be adjusted to brush the work until the Brush is entirely worn out, and also performs the function of keeping the last lower Feed Roller free from the dust, which is so liable to stick to it, and mar the finish of the work done.

Every part of the Machine is numbered. Duplicate pieces can be furnished at once. All high speed Shafting is made of steel. Wear of parts can be taken up. All Boxes are lined with the best babbitt. All Cylinders turned very true. All parts of Machine adjustable. One thousand Machines now in operation.

What we claim for our Machinery: Speed; ease of operation and adjustment to different classes of work; superior quality of work done; durability and thorough construction.

Parties ordering will please mention whether they will be driven by belt coming through the floor, or from line shafting, on same flat as Machine.

Belting required where Counter is located four feet from Machine: One belt 9 feet, three inches wide; one belt 10 feet, three inches wide; one belt 16 feet 6 inches, four inches wide; one belt 14 feet, four inches wide; one belt 6 feet 6 inches, one and one-half inches wide. Counter should make 465 revolutions per minute.

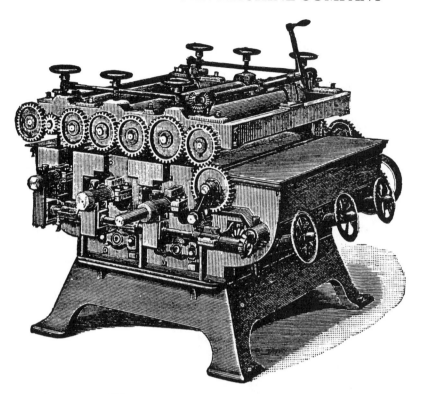

The Invincible Sander.

The above cut represents our new Wood Polisher, called the "Invincible," and which we submit for your inspection and trial.

Our first aim in the making of this new Machine was to insure more perfect and uniform work than could be done by hand. After accomplishing this, we directed our attention to making a Machine, which, in all its details, would be simple, compact, easy to adjust, yet of great strength and durability. As a result, we have the Invincible Sander--one which requires no expert or high-priced man to operate, and one that when adjustments are to be made can be done with accuracy, ease and dispatch.

We guarantee to put the sandpaper on the drums in one-third the time heretofore required and to save 25 per cent. of sandpaper over other machines

We dispense entirely with all screws and bolts for fastening the paper to the drums, and now use a mechanism which is simple and positive. Every part of the Machine is adjusted with screws, thus dispensing with all lagging, etc.

In the Machine will be found three Sand Cylinders. The two first ones are about the ordinary size, and are covered with a new kind of packing, which is very uniform and durable. The last Sand Drum is smaller, being only 7 inches in diameter, but it revolves much faster than the others, and has a very soft, fine Cushion for the paper, which is calculated to just touch the work,and impart a very high polish. The Sand Drums are all adjustable, and can be raised or lowered to a desired cut by simply turning the Hand Wheels, which are directly in front of Machine, beneath the Table. The Oscillator is simple, fast, strong, positive, and durable. There is no lost motion or wear, as there is in all cam movements, consequently no jar or tremor to the Machine.

The Bed Plates are cast very heavy, and are supported frombeneath, making it impossible to break them. The Frame is strong and heavy, and the whole Machine is one-half heavier than any other Sander offered to the public. Parties using more than one Machine, and of different sizes, need only keep one size of sandpaper. All shafting is very heavy and true, being the celebrated Hot-Polished Steel. Patent Self-Oiling loose Pulleys (14 x 8) furnished with theInvincible. Finest grade of Babbitt used in all boxes. Counter Shaft runs 550 revolution.

Machines are made in six sizes : 24,30,36,42,48,54 inches in width.

Belting required with Counter 4 feet from Machines : One belt 15 feet,six inches wide ; one belt 15 feet 6 inches, six inches wide ; one belt 13 feet 8 inches, six inches wide ; one belt 15 feet, four inches wide. Weights : 24, 4,000 ; 30, 4,500; 36, 5,000 ; 42, 5,500 ; 48, 6,200 pounds.

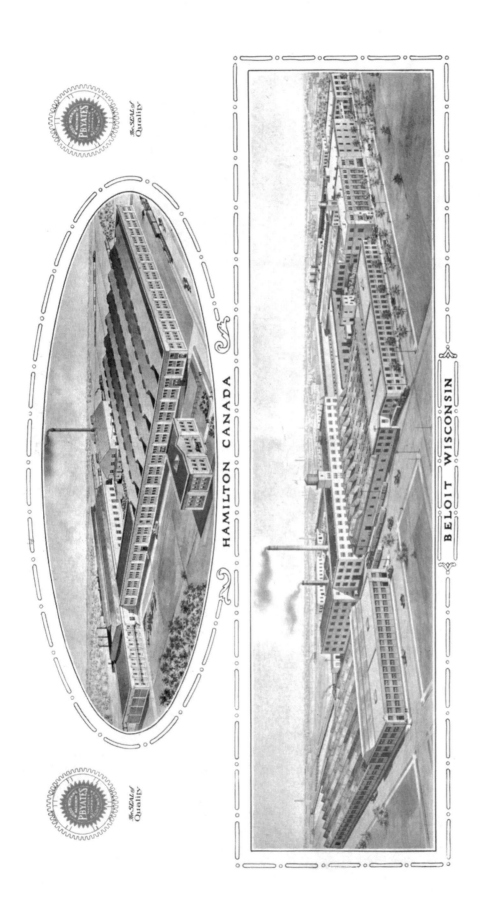

HAMILTON CANADA

BELOIT WISCONSIN

The SEAL of Quality

P. B. Yates Machine Co.

BELOIT, WISCONSIN. U.S.A.

Canadian Plant with Offices, Hamilton, Ontario

Paid Capital Stock, $2,500,000.   Plants cover Forty-two Acres.   Total Floor Space, 760,000 Square Feet.

Sectional Catalog circa 1918

No. 411 Single-Drum Sander

AN especially valuable machine for the small manufacturer is the No. 411 as shown. Where an extra fine finish is not required stock can be fed into this sander direct from a small resaw and, with coarse paper on the drum, it will be finished smoothly and uniformly. A finer finish, of course, results from first planing stock, and then sanding with fine paper on the drum.

The No. 411 has several of the improvements embodied in our larger Roll-Feed Sanders, such as Spiral Drums and Instantaneous Feed Change Device, permitting the operator choice of three rates of feed, by simply throwing a lever. The drums are of the same diameter as used on the larger machines and oscillate in the same manner. Note that there are no parts projecting above the top frame to hinder passing stock over the machine.

SPECIFICATIONS

Size	Approx. Floor Space	Approx. Horse Power	Reg. Drive	Coupler R. P. M.	Domestic Ship. Wt.	Boxed for Export	
						Wt. Lbs.	Cu. ft.
30″x8″	5′6″x32″ lg.	7½	12″ dia. T & L	500	2958	3250 gr. 2750 net	91½
42″x8″	6′6″x32″ lg.	10	12″ dia. T & L	500	3341	3725 gr. 3125 net	115

Weights and cubic contents given are approximate.

Yates 1917 Catalog No. 14

No. 421 Six-Drum Roll-Feed Sander

THIS machine was designed to sand large flat work, such as doors, veneers, etc., at one operation.

With the exception of the top frame, this machine is constructed like the No. 401 Triple Drum Sander. The top frame is carried by four hoist screws and supported by four two-inch guide posts. The top and bottom drums work in opposite directions, giving the stock an exceptionally high polish.

The oscillating mechanism is of the improved link type furnished on all Yates Drum Sanders.

The top frame may be raised or lowered either by hand or power. Separate or simultaneous adjustment of bottom drums is provided. Reverse feed device is an exclusive Yates feature.

SPECIFICATIONS

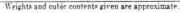

Size	Approx. Floor Space	Approx. Horse Power	Reg. Drive	Counter R. P. M.	Domestic Ship. Wt.	Boxed for Export	
						Wt. Lbs.	Cu. ft.
31"x 8"	64¾" lg. x 74" w.	15	14" dia. T & L	850	3111	3500 gr. 2850 net	96
49"x 8"	64¾" lg. x 94⅝" w.	30	14" dia. T & L	850	3264	3700 gr. 3000 net	111

Weights and cubic contents given are approximate.

No. 421 Motor Drive

Yates 1917 Catalog No. 14

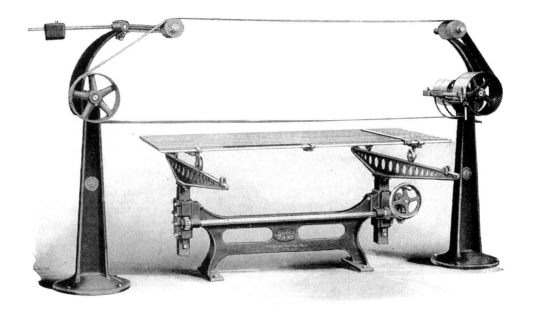

No. 430 Flexible Hand-Block Belt Sander

THIS machine will appeal especially to contractors and builders, cabinet workers, carriage and wagon shops, and small woodworking plants, as it is well adapted to light work.

The end stands are of a new type, being cast in the I-beam form of construction. This construction makes them exceptionally strong for the amount of metal they contain. The working face of the belt is 40" from the floor, the easiest working height.

The table is 30x80 inches, supported by two large square columns from a cast iron base. These columns move up and down in machined ways by means of a rack and pinion, operated through a worm gear and convenient hand-wheel. Adjustment of table up and down is 8".

Sand belt pulleys will take sand belt 8" wide, but a 6" belt is regularly furnished. The sand belt drive pulley is rubber covered and provided with tight and loose pulley drive. Adjustable sand belt tightener with counter weight is furnished. Can also be furnished motor drive.

SPECIFICATIONS

Max. Size Stock	Approx. Floor Space	Approx. Horse Power	Reg. Drive	Counter R. P. M.	Domestic Ship. Wt.	Boxed for Export	
						Wt. Lbs.	Cu. ft.
42" w. x 9" thick	10'2"x5'9"	2	8" dia. T & L	760	1326	1875 gr. 1200 net	79½

Weights and cubic contents given are approximate.

Yates 1917 Catalog No. 14

THE YATES-AMERICAN MACHINE COMPANY

Type S-2 Edge Sander

THE Type S-2 is distinctly original in design, having many mechanical and operating features found on no other edge sander.

The base is cast in one piece, flaring out at the floor. It is open at the rear, giving access to the working parts inside.

The principal working parts consist of two vertical spindles, one at each end of the machine. Both the driven spindle and the small sanding spindle carry covered drums. Around these a 10″ endless sand belt travels. At the same time the spindles are made to oscillate vertically by means of an eccentric shaft and a link. The small spindle runs in ball bearings, and is supported by a strong bracket to eliminate vibration.

The manner of driving the oscillator shaft is new. The reducing pulley is mounted on the arm of a lever, the other arm of which extends outside the machine. By pushing this lever down the oscillator drive belts are tightened and become operative.

Special drums and forms can be furnished to sand scroll work, or individual designs of practically any nature.

SPECIFICATIONS

Max. Size Stock	Approx. Floor Space	Approx. Horse Power	Reg. Drive	Counter R. P. M.	Domestic Ship. Wt.	Boxed for Export	
						Wt. Lbs.	Cu. ft.
42″x10″	68″x34″	4	10″ dia. T & L	325	2015	2375 gr. 1875 net	102

Weights and cubic contents given are approximate.

Yates 1917 Catalog No. 14

41

No. 199 Hand Planer

THIS machine is designed for small planing mills, manual training shops, pattern shops, etc.

The base is cast-in-one-piece and vibrationless. Two-knife round cutterhead is regularly furnished. Both tables adjust horizontally and the front table vertically by means of a hand-wheel.

The universal guide is adjustable across the table and at an angle for bevel jointing. The safety guard is of special design. It is easily operated and drops out of the way for head adjustment.

SPECIFICATIONS

Size	Approx. Floor Space	Approx. Horse Power	Reg. Drive	Counter R. P. M.	Domestic Ship. Wt.	Boxed for Export	
						Wt. Lbs.	Cu. ft.
12"x7'	31" wide x 86½" long	2½	8" dia. T & L	1125	2091	2475 gr. 1900 net	33
16"x7'	35" wide x 86½" long	2½	8" dia. T & L	1125	2142	2550 gr. 1950 net	38
20"x7'	39" wide x 86½" long	3½	8" dia. T & L	1125	2269	2775 gr. 2125 net	45
24"x7'	43" wide x 86½" long	3½	8" dia. T & L	1125	2321	2875 gr. 2225 net	54
30"x7'	49" wide x 86½" long	5	8" dia. T & L	1125	2550	3150 gr. 2500 net	65

Weights and cubic contents given are approximate.

Rear View of Yates No. 199 Showing Motor Drive

Yates 1917 Catalog No. 14

No. 213 Continuous Feed
Glue Jointer

THE No. 213 is designed to make straight glue joints with speed and precision.

The base is a vibrationless one-piece casting with wide floor flanges.

Straight jointer heads with three-inch face are regularly furnished. Positive and accurate feed is secured by mechanism consisting of milled lugs fastened to the links of a heavy roller chain. A small hand-wheel adjusting infeed table is an exclusive feature. An attachment on outfeed table keeps short stock from falling off.

A glueing attachment is furnished on special order.

SPECIFICATIONS

Size Stock	Approx. Floor Space	Approx. Horse Power	Reg. Drive	Counter R. P. M.	Domestic Ship. Wt.	Boxed for Export	
						Wt. Lbs.	Cu. ft.
¼″ to 3″ thick	63¾″ wide x 122″ long	7	12″ dia. T & L	1125	4463	5225 gr. 4225 net	202

Weights and cubic contents given are approximate.

Yates No. 213 Showing Motor Drive

Yates 1917 Catalog No. 14

N-1 Shaper

THE purpose of this machine is to provide the trade with a shaper adapted to either belt or motor drive, and provided with those refined details of construction which have been found so important through our experience during recent years.

The machine is built on massive lines, not only to secure the freedom from vibration so necessary in a shaper, but also to attain long wear and the utmost freedom from mechanical troubles.

The table is of generous proportions, accurately machined, and firmly fastened to the base with heavy bolts. Detachable spindles will be furnished regularly. The column supports for the top spindle bearing are large and carefully machined. The upper spindle bearing itself when used is a bronze bushing. Not needed with heads 6" and under. Spindles 1½" diameter, 30" apart. The table bearing, as well as the bottom bearing, is the latest type high speed ball bearing. These bearings are the same type in both motor and belt drive forms of the machine. A gravity feeding oil system amply lubricates both the table and bottom bearings. Regular head 6". Special heads up to 12" long.

In the direct motor drive machine each motor has its own oil switch, also a "no load" and "over load" release, located, one at either end of the frame. Each switch is operated with a hand lever. Both motors may be cut out by means of the foot pedal at front of machine.

Spindles are raised and lowered by hand wheels. Motor R.P.M. 7200. Belt R.P.M. 7000.

SPECIFICATIONS

Size	Approx. Floor Space	Approx. Horse Power	Reg. Drive	Counter R. P. M.	Domestic Ship. Wt.	Boxed for Export	
						Wt. Lbs.	Cu. ft.
40"x72"	40"x72"	5	12" dia. T & L	1125	3500	3700 gr. 3300 net	55

Weights and cubic contents given are approximate.

Yates 1917 Catalog No. 14

44

Yates 1917 Catalog No. 14

No. 232 Swing Cut-Off Saw

THE Yates No. 232 is a small sized cut-off saw of exceptional durability. It is just the machine for the smaller mills, and will give many years of constant and efficient service. Built for wall attachment.

The saw frame is 36" in length, and cast in one piece with strong braces. This frame pivots at points just below the countershaft boxes, thus keeping the same free from countershaft vibration. The frame, being hung in this manner, also keeps the belt tight at all times.

An adjustable counterpoise insures a quick and easy return of the saw after each cut.

The No. 232 is built in a slightly modified form for direct motor drive, as shown in cut on this page.

No. 232 With Motor Drive

SPECIFICATIONS

Size	Approx. Floor Space	Approx. Horse Power	Reg. Drive	Counter R. P. M.	Domestic Ship. Wt.	Boxed for Export	
						Wt. Lbs.	Cu. ft.
14" or 16" saw	none	3	8" dia. T & L	750	457	500 gr. 400 net	20

Weights and cubic contents given are approximate.

Yates No. 232 Swing Cut-Off Saw

YATES No. 238 TRIM SAW

THIS machine is a most practical and economical tool for squaring the ends of small stock such as flooring, ceiling, moulding, etc. An operator can trim a great deal more of such stock in a day on the No. 238 than on the ordinary swing cut-off saw, because he doesn't have to do everything with his hands.

The No. 238 is virtually a swing saw reversed. The swing arm is swung from below and mounted on trunnion-point set screws. This allows any side play or lost motion to be easily taken up. The arm is counterbalanced by means of springs, which act much more quickly than weights.

Instead of the usual hand-pull of a swing cut-off saw, the saw is brought into the cut by means of a foot treadle 22" wide. Pressure applied at any point of this wide treadle brings the saw down to its stop, making it impossible to swing beyond that point. When the cut is made the operator removes his foot from the treadle, and springs instantly return the saw to its original position. A guard prevents danger of accident to the operator.

The work table is placed at an angle of 45° and is provided with an edge gauge at the bottom against which the stock rests by its own weight. This insures an accurate cut, whether the operator is careful to hold the stock up against the straight edge or not.

Stock up to 8" wide and 3" thick can be handled by using a 14-inch saw. One saw of this size is regularly furnished with each machine.

Yates Sectional Catalog ca. 1918

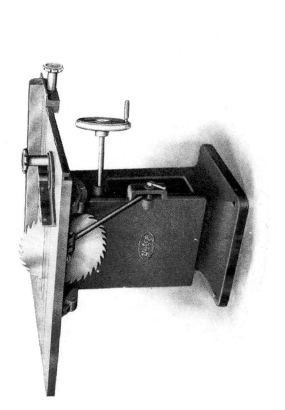

Yates 1917 Catalog No. 14

No. 226 Saw Table

THE No. 226 Saw Table is exactly similar to the No. 225, illustrated and described on opposite page, with the exception of a boring attachment, which consists of a bracket carrying a cross head, bolted securely to base of the machine with four large cap screws. Large cored holes are provided to allow shavings to drop through.

SPECIFICATIONS

Size	Approx. Floor Space	Approx. Horse Power	Reg. Drive	Counter R. P. M.	Domestic Ship. Wt.	Boxed for Export	
						Wt. Lbs.	Cu. ft.
14" or 16" saw	48" w x 79½" lg.	3½	8" dia. T & L	1125	1275	1450 gr. 1200 net	43

Weights and cubic contents given are approximate.

No. 225 Saw Table

THIS saw table is well adapted for use in all shops and plants where odd jobs of ripping and cut-off work are to be done.

Base is cast-in-one-piece, and widely flanged at floor line, eliminating vibration.

The table is heavy and accurately planed. It can be tilted to a maximum angle of 45 degrees.

SPECIFICATIONS

Size	Approx. Floor Space	Approx. Horse Power	Reg. Drive	Counter R. P. M.	Domestic Ship. Wt.	Boxed for Export	
						Wt. Lbs.	Cu. ft.
14" or 16" saw	48" w x 79½" lg.	3½	8" dia. T & L	1125	1275	1450 gr. 1200 net	43

Weights and cubic contents given are approximate.

YATES No. 185 GEARLESS DOUBLE SURFACER

Yates Sectional Catalog ca. 1918 — see next page

Yates No. 185 Gearless Double Surfacer

The design and construction of the No. 185 Double Surfacer especially adaps it to surfacing box shook stock in original or short lengths, to sash and door factory, and to average planing mill work. It is not in the high-speed class; but it combines good speed with fine surfacing and an ability to stand up indefinitely under the hard work given such machines in the average factory or mill.

The No.185 may be had either with or without our hopper feeding feature. In many cases, not only in box factories, but in sash and door plants as well, the 185 might very well use a hopper feed to good advantage. It increases the output of the machine in a remarkable manner and certainly pays for the small additional cost.

Drive is regularly furnished as illustrated. This gives a very compact, self-contained and powerful drive, as each belt is acted upon by a gravity tightener. However, when specified, the 185 will be furnished with short table and drive arranged overhead or at rear or front beneath floor.

The four 12-inch feed rolls of the 185 are powerfully driven by roller bearing chains. The only gears used on the machine are in the variable speed device. The use of chains, instead of gears, insures a very low upkeep through the life of the machine.

The top infeeding roll is corrugated for additional driving power, and is sectional to permit feeding stock or uneven thickness. The other rolls are plain. Pressure is supplied by large coil springs, which have a yield of one inch.

Round cutter-heads equipped with thin steel knives are regularly supplied. Provision is made for sharpening the knives without removal from heads. the $2\frac{3}{8}$" journals run in babbitted bearings 10" long. The top head cuts first, and as the infeeding bed is solid, the "flutter" incident to the surfacing of thin stock on some machines is entirely absent. The 185 is much used as a thin stock surfacer for this reason.

The hold-down after the cut is adjustable for thickness of stock. The bottom head, the platen after cut, and the lower outfeeding roll, are all simultaneously adjustable, by means of the squared-end shaft under the bottom head pulley. Each is also separately adjustable for alignment. The bottom head may be lowered so that the machine may be used as a single surfacer, or it may be raised to equalize cuts of both heads. A bottom head jointer is provided.

Four heavy posts support the top yoke at points close to the roll bearings and afford a rigid bearing for the upper working parts. Vibration, even with the top up to the limit of 8" above the bed line is unnoticeable in the work of the machine.

The chipbreaker is sectional and pressure is applied to each section by heavy coil springs. Tension on these springs is adjustable. The chipbreaker is adjustable, and has a yield of one inch against its spring to allow each section to follow the contour of the stock face.

The bed line of the 185 is 32" above the floor, a very convenient height for the average operator, one that will not tire him as quickly as either a lower or a higher bed.

No gears, chains, sprocket wheels, or other working parts are exposed. Guards cover everything to protect workmen and comply with all state laws.

The base and frame of the machine are cast in one piece. The bottom of the frame casting has a wide flange which gives the machine wide bearing on the floor. Thus the foundation for the working parts of the 185 is absolutely rigid, insuring good work and long life to the machine.

Rates of Feed: 30, 75 and 100 feet per minute.

The No. 185 is built in but one size: 30 x 8 inches.

11,000 pounds.

Yates Sectional Catalog ca. 1918

Yates No. 70 Automatic Turning Machine

No. 70 Automatic Turning Machine

THE distinct characteristics of this machine are—large capacity, automatic precision and fine finish. Turns round, square, hexagonal, octagonal, straight faced, sharp cornered and tapered patterns.

Base is cast-in-one-piece, heavy, absorbs all vibration.

The shape of the finished pattern is determined by the shape of a steel die fitted to the drive center, which revolves with the stock against an adjustable shoe. Stock is moved alternately to and from the revolving knives and shaped to the same form as the die.

Turning of stock to pattern is entirely automatic. Carriage rides on roller bearings, and is controlled by convenient lever.

SPECIFICATIONS

Size	Approx. Floor Space	Approx. Horse Power	Reg. Drive	Counter R. P. M.	Domestic Ship. Wt.	Boxed for Export	
						Wt. Lbs.	Cu. ft.
32″ lg.	33¾″ w. x 72″ lg.	7	10″ dia. T & L	650	2751	3000 gr. 2600 net	152
42″ lg.	33¾″ w. x 82″ lg.	7	10″ dia. T & L	650	2950	3300 gr. 2800 net	161

Weights and cubic contents given are approximate.

No. 70   Motor Driven

Yates 1917 Catalog No. 14

50

Type G-2 Edging and Ripping Saw with Traveling Bed

THE purpose of this machine is to make a straight line cut without the aid of a ripping guide. Crooked, tapering, or wane edged stock is easily run, and good lumber may be saved from stock with bad centers. Pieces run for glue jointing often need no additional operation.

The perfect straight line cut is made possible by means of a single endless-chain traveling bed, running just beneath saw and pressure rolls. Chain is of roller type with extra large links running over strong cut sprockets. Milled feed blocks are fastened to chain and hold stock in place.

Base is cast in one piece, and widely flanged at floor line, forming a vibrationless foundation.

Table is 34½" above floor, 61" long, 34" wide. The table is in two sections and separated by thin brass laminations. Occasional removal of one of these compensates for any lateral wear of chain blocks.

The pressure rolls are three in number and idle. The tapered hold-down rolls are 3½", placed at either side of saw. Feed operated from gear box. All gears run in grease. Dust spout removes 95% of all saw dust.

An exclusive and recently patented feature is an efficient "kick-back" guard. Can also be furnished motor driven.

SPECIFICATIONS

Stock Size	Approx. Floor Space	Approx. Horse Power	Reg. Drive	Counter R. P. M.	Domestic Ship. Wt.	Boxed for Export	
						Wt. Lbs.	Cu. ft.
Thickest 4" Shortest 10"	61" w. x 56" lg.	7½	7" dia. Tgt. Pul.	775	3850	4050 gr. 3700 net	118

Weights and cubic contents given are approximate.

Yates Type G-2 Edging & Ripping Saw with Traveling Bed

Yates 1917 Catalog No. 14

No. 52 Scroll Saw

THE machine illustrated on the opposite page is our 36-inch Scroll Saw. The frame is heavy, cast in one piece, and the weight is so distributed as to yield the greatest rigidity.

The wheels are 36 inches in diameter with forged steel rims and polished steel spokes. They have a 2-inch face, rubber covered, and are perfectly balanced.

The table is 30x38 inches, extra strong, with 45-degree front tilt and 5-degree rear tilt.

All needed adjustments can be made from the front of the machine. Pulleys, 12x4½ inches; saw, 18 ft. 6 inches; cuts stock 16 inches thick; sawing space, 16x36 inches. Wire or iron guards on special order.

SPECIFICATIONS

Size	Approx. Floor Space	Approx. Horse Power	Reg. Drive	Counter R. P. M.	Domestic Ship. Wt.	Boxed for Export	
						Wt. Lbs.	Cu. ft.
36″ wheel	59½″ x 43½″	2	12″ dia. T & L	500	1734	2050 gr. 1600 net	126

Weights and cubic contents given are approximate.

No. 52 Motor Drive

Yates No. 52 Scroll Saw

No. 281 Roll-Feed Band Rip Saw

THE No. 281 Roll-Feed Band Rip Saw is a unit that combines the highest possible production with the greatest economy in material, labor and power consumption.

The base is cast in one piece, and widely flanged at floor line, assuring freedom from vibration.

The upper 44-inch band wheel is carried on a heavy cross head, adjustable vertically on the dove-tail slides of the heavy, upright column. This cross-head structure also supports the knife-edge straining device—a very sensitive mechanism that effectually safeguards the blade under all ordinary operating conditions. Built R. or L. H.

The feed works consist of two sets of power driven rolls. The lower, smooth set is inserted in the table and the upper, fluted set carried by a cross head adjustable vertically on the upright column. Each roll is mounted independently and carried on brackets. Each roll has a separate yield, effectually compensating for all irregularities and variation of stock thickness. The rolls are chain driven from a sprocket on the feed works driving shaft. Maximum Stock sizes 20" wide, 12" thick.

SPECIFICATIONS

Size	Approx. Floor Space	Approx. Horse Power	Reg. Drive	Arbor R. P. M.	Domestic Ship. Wt.	Boxed for Export	
						Wt. Lbs.	Cu. ft.
4" saw	5'8"x6'3"	10	20" dia. Tight	690	5202	6075 gr. 4750 net	265
5" saw	5'8"x6'3"	10	20" dia. Tight	690	5202	6075 gr 4750 net	265

Weights and cubic contents given are approximate.

Yates No. 281 Roll-Feed Band Rip Saw

No. 108 Open-Side Moulder

THE Yates No. 108 Open-Side Moulder combines the good features of both the Inside and Outside types, with none of the faults of either.

The base is cast in one piece, of the bridge type.

The four feed rolls are 8" in diameter and are driven by wide-faced gears cut to perfect mesh. Power is transmitted to the lower rolls by a pinion through a large gear, and this same source drives the upper rolls through a roller-bearing chain, automatically kept at proper tension at all times.

A left-side guide for short stock extends from in-end to just before side head, and is adjustable. The adjustable hold-down after top head may be thrown back out of operator's way when setting up. It is locked rigidly when in position. Adjustable brackets are provided to receive center hold-down extending from top to bottom head.

Side head spindles have both crosswise and vertical adjustment, also tilting adjustment of $22\frac{1}{2}$ degrees.

All adjustments are made from one side of machine.

SPECIFICATIONS

Size	Approx. Floor Space	Approx. Horse Power	Reg. Drive	Counter R. P. M.	Domestic Ship. Wt.	Boxed for Export	
						Wt. Lbs.	Cu. ft.
10"x8"	92⅞" w. x 134¼" lg.	20	14" dia. T & L	850	6592	7200 gr. 6100 net	248
12"x8"	94⅞" w. x 134¼" lg.	25	14" dia. T & L	850	8094	8200 gr. 7500 net	345
15"x8"	97⅞" w. x 134¼" lg.	30	14" dia. T & L	850	8446	9400 gr. 7900 net	360

Weights and cubic contents given are approximate.

Yates 1917 Catalog No. 14

Type A-1 Planer and Matcher

THIS machine is designed for high class work at medium speeds.

The base is cast in one piece. Four-knife square top and bottom cutter heads, and four-knife square heads are furnished. Round, or combination heads, with thick, thin and ground-to-pattern knives for moulding, can be furnished at extra cost. The yoke which carries the bottom head may be drawn out for convenience in grinding and changing knives. The cut of bottom head is altered by lever which raises or lowers the two lower infeed rolls and bed before same. The bottom head may be dropped beneath bed by lever immediately under it. The side head spindles are carried in heavy matcher legs and supported by two matcher bars. Vertical adjustment can be made while machine is in operation. Chipbreaker for top head is sectional, and pressure is applied by means of spring.

The feed works consist of six 7" rolls, four infeed and two outfeed. The drive consists of heavy roller bearing chains working over cut sprockets. Levers at both ends of machine control rates of feed.

SPECIFICATIONS

Size	Approx. Floor Space	Approx. Horse Power	Reg. Drive	Counter R. P. M.	Domestic Ship. Wt.	Boxed for Export	
						Wt. Lbs.	Cu. ft.
15"x6"	92⅜" w.x 143½" lg.	30	14" dia. T & L	1125	11367	12500 gr. 10325 net	325
24"x8"	101⅜" w.x 143½" lg.	40	14" dia. T & L	1125	11897	12775 gr. 10830 net	326

Weights and cubic contents given are approximate.

Yates 1917 Catalog No. 14

Chapter 3

THE DEFIANCE MACHINE WORKS

"Every Market of the World"

In the early years of this country, Americans moved themselves and their goods in wagons built, one way or another, of wood. But demand never exceeded the production capacity of local wagon-builders, wheelwrights, and blacksmiths. Things changed, however, in 1849 when gold was discovered in California and a vast westward migration of settlers began. Their demand for all kinds of wagons, in addition to the great transportation needs of both North and South during the Civil War, called for organized factories and new machinery.

During this period, highly specialized machines were designed and built for every aspect of wagon building. Sophisticated machines were developed for boring, turning, and mortising hubs; turning, tenoning, and shaving spokes; truing and finishing wheel assemblies; felloe-bending; as well as more common machines for drilling, planing, sawing, jointing, and sanding.

One early company soon came to dominate this market and continued to do so for almost 100 years – The Defiance Machine Works of Defiance, Ohio, founded by Peter Kettenring.

Kettenring was born January 10, 1835, in the Rhine district of Germany. In 1836 the family emigrated to the United States and in 1838 homesteaded 360 acres of unimproved government land in Henry County, Ohio, 12 miles southwest of Defiance. In the spring of 1844 they moved to Defiance, a town located at the confluence of three rivers. Because of the availability of water-power, large machine shops, flour mills, and fac-

tories located here for the purpose of making agricultural implements, sashes, blinds, and wagons.

In 1849 Peter started a two-year apprenticeship as a molder at the small foundry of Kimball & Frank, which employed about six hands. Afterwards he worked as a molder in Toledo, Ohio, and Fort Wayne, Indiana.

In a sense, what would become The Defiance Machine Works, was the city's oldest industry. It began in 1849, when a combination foundry and machine shop was built and leased to Kimball & Frank, the former a molder, the latter a machinist.

In 1856 Kettenring returned to Defiance and leased the foundry where he had served as an apprentice. He began business with a cash capital of $125 and for the first six months employed only two men. By 1870, he was in business with two partners; they employed fifteen men, and the plant covered some 800 square feet.

During these early years, the company only manufactured woodworking machinery used mainly for building wagons, carriages, wooden vehicle wheels of all types, handles, spools, bobbins, hoops, insulator pins, neckyokes, and singletrees. Later would come machines for shaping automobile bodies and wheels, baseball bats, golf club shafts, etc. The various wagon and buggy factories in the United States and abroad were almost exclusively equipped with Defiance machines.

A stock company was organized in 1872 and incorporated in 1875 under the name Defiance Machine Works. Besides woodworking machinery, the company now built steam engines, boilers, shafting, pulleys, hangers, plows, etc., together with all kinds of custom castings and general jobbing work. The size of the business steadily increased; in 1882 some 125 hands were employed.

An 1892 catalog listed just part of the 300 different classes of woodworking machinery manufactured by the company – some quite exotic by modern standards. There were such things as wheel boxing machines, felloe benders, variety lathes, sanders, hub mortisers, bandsaws, rip saws, planers, jointers, and swing cut off saws.

The company vigorously pursued overseas sales of its wheel- and wagon-making machinery. Defiance was to wheel- and wagon-making what the Japanese are to cars and electronics today. In the mid-1890s, European sales increased dramatically. Twenty five machines were sold to a plant in Zurich, Switzerland, and a number to a plant in Christiana, Norway; single examples of many machines were sold in other cities. The result was that there was hardly a city of any size in the world where a Defiance machine was not hard at work.

The great variety and number of machines manufactured by the Works is evident from its 208 page 1895 catalog; the company issued 5000 copies, with illustrations and descriptions of machines ranging from $75 to $1500.

Defiance catalog No. 200, dated 1910, is one of the finest woodworking machinery catalogs ever issued. 533 pages long, it is illustrated with superb engravings of the 255 basic machines then making up the line. Options and variations broadened the line even more.

The 12" Hand-Feed Planing and Jointing Machine is a typical example of a machine from this period. The frame of the 1000 pound iron machine was cast in one piece, with a cored center, making a rigid surface to properly support the working parts and hold them in perfect alignment. The tables, measuring 62" over all, were planed true and raised and lowered in V slides with adjustment for wear. The round, forged steel cutterhead carried three high speed steel knives. Accurately balanced, with journals ground true, it ran in genuine babbitt metal self-lubricating bearings, enclosed to keep out dust and grit. The fence could be adjusted over the entire surface of the table to any angle or bevel even while the machine was running. The shavings from the cutter were discharged at the rear of the machine through a chamber cored through the frame, always depositing them in one place and never scattering them all over the shop floor or inside the frame. A blower pipe could also be attached to the opening. It required 3 horse power to drive the machine. The jointer could also be purchased with a boring attachment.

During the early years of World War I, the company also became a major supplier of machinery for building artillery and gun carriage wheels. By 1915 the Works was building 90% of all the machinery used in making military, as well as sporting, rifle stocks, both in the U.S. and abroad. For many years it had built practically all of the artillery wheel and military vehicle machinery used in government arsenals throughout the world. It had the unique distinction of having directly supplied 20 of the leading governments of the world with woodworking machines for use in their arsenals and shipyards.

By the time the United States entered the war, the Works was building many special munitions-making machines that could not be purchased elsewhere. All woodworking machinery produced during the period was principally devoted to machines for making wheels, rifle stocks, propellers, struts, side bars for saddletrees, and handles for trenching tools.

After the war, horizontal boring mills, heavy duty drilling machines, rail drills, turret screw machines, and valve grinders were all added. Large orders for these new machines, which required larger castings, led to the construction of a new state-of-the-art foundry in 1920. At this time the Works reached its peak employment, with almost 700 hands (including 150 in the engineering department), and a plant with 200,000 square feet of floor space covering three entire city blocks.

Between 1918 and 1921 the Works designed and built special machine tools for rapid production of gas and gasoline engines and various car, truck, and tractor parts. The line was successful, with machines sold to General Motors, The Willy Corp., Ansted Engineering Co., Timken-Detroit Co., Lincoln Motor Car Co., Hummer Engine Works, the Packard Motor Co., and others.

Unfortunately, the company was caught in a credit crunch by the post-war depression of 1921 and was forced into receivership. The receivership was dissolved in 1923, and the company continued in business until the Works was sold to The Toledo Scale Co. in 1938.

About 1937 the Works had cut back to three six-hour days. A beginning apprentice made 30¢ an hour then. One such apprentice, James Perry, remarked that "if one was respectful and interested, the old timers would go to any length to teach you their skills, but if you were lazy or a smart aleck you got little help."

Richard Vaugh of Columbus, Ohio, an ex-Defiance resident who delivered telegraph messages to the Works as a boy and worked briefly as a machinist at the Works (1940-41), believed the Works had quit making woodworking machinery in the early 1930s. Only machine tools were being made by 1940 – drill presses, boring mills, etc.

The Works' activity after Pearl Harbor in 1941 was to make even larger numbers of machine tools as quickly as possible. Immediately after the war, scales were made.

On March 1, 1949, The Defiance Machine Works shut down (except for maintenance work). It celebrated its 100th anniversary being dispersed under an auctioneer's gavel. The auction was held on September 20th and 21st, and the 1200-1500 units of machinery and equipment, valued at $1,500,000, attracted scores of bidders from all over the country. Most of the machine tools had been bought between 1942 and 1946 and included Defiance models. The only woodworking machines for sale were from the Works' own pattern shop and included band saws, table saws, jointers, planers, pattern maker's lathes, sanders, etc.

In a sense, the Defiance Machine Works would continue, due to the enterprise of apprentice James Perry. In 1937 Perry's father, who worked in the plant's foundry from 1906 until 1948, helped get 21-year-old James into the Work's four-year apprenticeship program.

After discharge from the Navy in 1946, James decided to start his own machine shop, despite the offer of a good job at the Works. Ironically, James's success depended on obtaining the drawings, patterns, etc., for the Defiance Handle and Variety Lathes. Sadly, these were the only woodworking machines for which there remained any demand for parts and tooling. The volume of the business was too small to interest the Works any more. Approached by James, the company generously gave him everything he needed and only charged him for the existing inventory of castings and finished parts.

James set up his machine shop in the basement of his home, and then got in touch with lathe owners. The response was great and his shop supplied them with everything they needed.

In 1950 James had to move the J.L. Perry Company to larger quarters. He was not only supplying lathe customers but also doing a large variety of other custom work for local industries and the public. In 1977 he retired and sold the business to Joseph Messerman.

The Messerman Machine Company, 407 Agnes Street, P.O. Box 116, Defiance, OH 43512, still supplies repair parts and accessories for the old Defiance 42" Automatic Handle Lathe, the 18" and 24" Automatic Handle Lathe, and the 32" Patent Variety Lathe. Messerman has many of the original patterns and even some blueprints.

WOOD-WORKING MACHINERY

THE DEFIANCE MACHINE WORKS

ESTABLISHED 1850

DEFIANCE, OHIO, U. S. A.

Defiance 1904 Catalog 194

26" Patent Six-Roll Double Surface Planer.

Net Weight, 10,000 Pounds.

see next page

26″ Patent Six-Roll Double Surface Planer.

THIS ENGRAVING represents our 26″ Patent Six-Roll Double Surface Planer, of new and original design, which contains many new patented features for convenience in adjustment, and the accuracy of its operation. It will plane, at one time, both sides of either hard or soft wood, and reduce the surface to a smooth, satin-like finish. It is, therefore, a great labor-saving device when used on work requiring a high polish, such as used by the makers of furniture, pianos, and interior woodwork. It is equally capable of handling heavy work where deep cutting on a coarse feed is required. Its capacity is sufficient to plane up to 26″ wide, and any size narrower up to 12″ thick, down to the thinnest panel, and it is highly recommended for the use of wagon, agricultural implement, railway car, and ship builders use.

THE FRAME is a massive casting of new design and of pleasing lines, with cored center and a wide floor base of sufficient weight to properly support the working parts and overcome all tendency to spring or jar.

THE CUTTER HEADS are made from solid crucible steel forgings, three-wing construction, each fitted with three knives and lipped for cross-grained or knotty lumber. The journals run in patent ring-oiling bearings $2\frac{3}{16}$″ diameter, 12″ long, which are automatically lubricated; with a patent pneumatic driving pulley at each end, with 5″ face, for the upper head, and 6″ for the lower, and they are fitted to the journals on taper bearings, avoiding the use of set screws or keys.

BOTH CUTTER HEADS are driven from a countershaft attached to the ceiling, which is provided with a special belt tightener so constructed to automatically secure the proper tension to the belt for the lower head, when raising and lowering the table; thus the floor space around the machine is entirely disencumbered, and the counter and pulleys are up out of the way. The lower cutter head, with its bearings, can be quickly removed from the machine, giving free access for the sharpening and setting of the knives. A gauge is furnished to accurately set the cutters from the center of the cutter head. By turning a single wrench the lower head can be adjusted up or down to regulate the depth of cut, or either end of the cutter head may be raised or lowered by the same wrench, and, by the use of an auxiliary bed attached to and forming a part of the main table, the cut of the lower head can be changed while the machine is in motion.

THE LOWER CUTTER HEAD is placed 4″ in advance of the upper one for the purpose of securing a true surface on the bottom of the material before the upper head commences to cut, which reduces all uneven surfaces and twists from the under surface of the material, thus providing a true line to which the upper surface is planed.

THE CHIP BREAKERS move in a true circle with the cutters, remaining the same distance from the knives when taking a light or heavy cut, a most essential feature for smooth planing, and they are hinged at the rear, and can be lifted back out of the way, giving free access to the upper head.

SHAVING CHUTES are fitted to each head to which can be easily attached a conveyor pipe of an exhauster.

THE TABLE is supported upon four heavy steel screws and fitted to the side of the frame at each corner, in broad guide ways, and it is raised and lowered by power, a slight movement of a single convenient hand lever controlling it, raising or lowering it accurately to a scale on the frame for different thicknesses of planing.

THE PATENT FEED consists of six large power-driven rolls, three above and three in the table, and they are rotated by gearing cut from the solid, which produces a perfectly steady motion, free from back-lash or chatter, which enables the machine to produce perfectly smooth planing.

THE FRONT UPPER FEED ROLL is constructed of roller sections, which enables a number of strips or boards of uneven thickness to be fed through the machine at one and the same time, and reduced to equal dimensions.

THE FEED, which is very powerful, has four changes of speed, 40, 50, 60, and 70 feet per minute, to suit the different kinds of work. It can be started, stopped, or changed from fast to slow, or the table raised or lowered by the operator without changing his position.

ALL THE JOURNALS and wearing surfaces are provided with self-oiling devices and so inclosed to prevent the admission of dust or dirt. The lubrication throughout has been given special attention, and all the oil reservoirs are bored from the solid, there being no core sand to work into the bearings.

THE COUNTER: Shaft, 9 feet long, $2\frac{3}{16}$″ diameter; three ball and socket adjustable drop hangers; two driving pulleys, 26″ × 5½″ for the upper head; one driver, 26″ × 6½″, for lower head; one driver each, 16″ × 3½″, and 18″ × 3½″ to drive subcounter on machine. Auxiliary counter for lower head: shaft, $1\frac{15}{16}$″ × 48″; one hanger; one special tightener; one pulley, 14″ × 6½″, with cross belt to 26″ × 6½″ pulley on main counter; one pulley, 12″ × 6½″, to drive lower head.

HORSE POWER to drive, 15; floor space occupied, 99″ × 66″.

Defiance 1904 Catalog 194

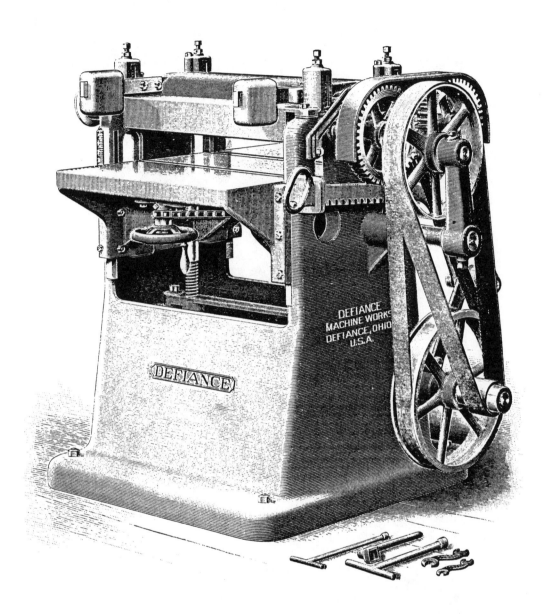

24" Patent Four Roll Single Surface Planer.

Net Weight, 2,000 Pounds.

Defiance 1910 Catalog 200

16″ Hand-Feed Planing and Jointing Machine.

Net Weight, 1,500 Pounds.

THE 16″ HAND-FEED PLANING AND JOINTING MACHINE, as shown by the engraving, is in general use by leading wood-working shops throughout the world. It is adapted to a wide range of uses and performs the work in a superior manner, more accurately and effecting an immense saving over hand labor, and it is recommended for straight planing, squaring up, taking out of wind, cornering, chamfering, beveling, and making glue jointings. It is suited to all the general requirements of sash, door, furniture, pattern, car, wagon, carriage, and agricultural implement manufacturers.

THE COUNTER is furnished as follows: Shaft, $1\frac{11}{16}''\times40''$; tight and loose pulleys, $10''\times5''$; driver, $20''\times4''$; speed, 1,000 rotations per minute; pulley on cutter head spindle, $4''\times4''$; speed, 5,000 rotations per minute.

HORSE POWER to drive, 4; floor space occupied, $28''\times84''$.

Defiance 1904 Catalog 194

No. 1 Patent 36″ Band, Scroll, and Rip Sawing Machine.

Net Weight, 1,400 Pounds.

see next page

No. 1 Patent 36″ Band, Scroll, and Rip Sawing Machine.

THIS ENGRAVING represents our new No. 1 Patent 36″ Band, Scroll, and Rip Sawing Machine, which contains many new patented features found in no other machine offered for this work. It is capable of carrying a saw blade as narrow as ⅛″, suitable for the very finest scroll sawing, such as required in piano and organ factories, pattern work, planing mills, and other similar classes of work. Also for the heavier kinds of sawing, such as cutting out plow beams, wagon and carriage wood stock, agricultural implement parts, etc., from hard woods, using a saw blade as wide as 2″. The adjustments on this machine are so perfect that it can be run constantly on light or heavy work, without the fear of injury to the saw blade or the machine.

THE FRAME, of neat design, is cast in one piece, with cored center, making it strong and reliable, and it is provided with a broad floor base to stand firm.

THE SADDLE, which supports the upper wheel, is accurately fitted to the frame in planed angle ways, scraped to an accurate bearing. It is adjustable up and down by hand wheel and screw to accommodate various lengths of saw blades, taking at the longest a saw 18½ feet.

THE WHEELS are 36″ in diameter, 2½″ face, covered with a solid endless rubber band ¼″ thick; they are ground perfectly true and balanced by our patent centrifugal balancing machine, making them capable of obtaining a high rate of speed without any vibration whatever. An ingenious spring device is used in connection with the upper wheel, to secure the exact amount of tension to the saw blade, which instantly accommodates itself for light or heavy sawing, unlike the old style weight affair, which is cumbersome and slow to act. It is a well-known fact that a spring will act one hundred times quicker than a weight, which means that a spring tension will meet and correct one hundred variations in the strain of a saw while a weight is getting in motion to take care of one, and very likely, because of its inertia, missing that. The saw will cut perfect work only when the tension is accurate. By a single hand screw, the upper saw wheel can be tilted, while running, to lead the saw to any path desired over the face of the wheels.

THE TABLE, of iron, is 30″ × 34″, planed true on top and arranged to tilt for bevel work to 45 degrees angle. It is fitted with a patent rip saw gauge, and laid off in inches and fractions, to set the gauge the desired distance from the saw for straight sawing or ripping lumber; this gauge can be instantly placed on or removed from the machine.

THE SAW GUIDES are of the patent non-friction type, and they will not heat or injure the saw.

THIS MACHINE measures 36″ from the inside of the frame to the center of the table, and, when the guide stem is elevated to its highest position, will take work 12½″ thick.

ALL THE SPINDLES are of forged steel and run in long self-lubricating bearings.

THE TIGHT AND LOOSE PULLEYS are 14″ diameter, 4″ face, and provided with an improved belt shipping apparatus, to be operated from the front side of the machine, and they should run 500 turns per minute. The loose pulley is fitted with bronze bearings and self-oiling device.

HORSE POWER to drive, 1½; floor space occupied, 42″ × 60″.

Defiance 1904 Catalog 194

No. 4 Patent Power Feed Band Ripping Saw.

Net Weight, 3,800 Pounds.

see next page

No. 4 Patent Power Feed Band Ripping Saw.

THIS ENGRAVING shows our No. 4 Patent Power Feed Band Ripping Saw, which represents the very highest type of this class of machinery. It is perfectly safe to operate, there being no tendency to throw the stock back, as with a circular saw, and the saw kerf, being much less, effects a large saving in lumber, and it cuts much smoother and truer. It will take 30″ between the fence and saw blade, and any size narrower, and up to 12″ thick and under. It will saw the stock square or to any bevel, as the table is provided with a tilting adjustment, a most desirable feature for sawing out moulding blanks and other bevel work, which cannot be performed on any other power feed band ripping saw on the market. It also has the advantage of ripping exceedingly short or long material, as the feeding rolls are close together. All the adjustments are made from the working side of the machine. The starting and stopping, changing the rate of feed for sawing various widths and thicknesses of lumber, straight or beveling, all can be quickly made without the operator leaving his position.

THE FRAME, of modern design, is cast in one piece, with cored center, is very heavy and stiff, to overcome all tendency to spring or vibrate when doing the very heaviest class of work, and it is provided with an exceedingly wide floor base to stand firm.

THE TABLE is exceedingly large and roomy, and it is fitted with rollers both in front and behind the saw to prevent friction. It is plainly laid off, with a scale, in inches and fractions, to quickly set the gauge the desired distance from the saw. This gauge or fence can be used on either the right or left hand side of the saw, and it is equipped with a horizontal roller at the front end and two vertical rollers on top to remove as much friction as possible, to make the lumber pass through the machine with the greatest ease. The table can be instantly tilted to any angle up to 45 degrees to a scale underneath the table.

THE WHEELS are 44″ diameter, ground perfectly true, and balanced by our Patent Rotary Balancing Machine, making them capable of obtaining a high rate of speed, entirely free from vibration. The wheel spindles are of steel, extra heavy, and they rotate in long, self-lubricating bronze bearings. An ingenious spring device is used in connection with the upper wheel to secure the exact amount of tension to the saw blade, which instantly accommodates itself for light or heavy sawing, unlike the old style weight affair, which is cumbersome and slow to act. It is a well-known fact that a spring will act one hundred times quicker than a weight, which means that a spring tension will meet and correct one hundred variations in the strain of a saw while a weight is getting in motion to take care of one, and very likely, because of its inertia, missing that. The saw will cut perfect work only when the tension is accurate. By this new device, it is almost impossible to break or injure the saw, and the saw can be instantly placed on or off the machine. By the adjustment of a single hand screw, the upper saw wheel can be tilted, while running, to lead the saw to any path desired over the face of the wheels.

THE PATENT SAW GUIDES will not heat or injure the saw, enabling the machine to run constantly on the heaviest work.

THE FEED is very powerful. It is driven by cut gears, which furnish a perfectly steady motion, and it can be instantly adjusted to feed from 50 to 150 feet per minute, having four changes of feed. The feed rolls have a vertical adjustment by hand wheel to accommodate stock from 0 to 12″ thick, with an automatic vertical movement of one inch to accommodate variations in thickness of stock, so that boards or plank of different thicknesses can be fed through the machine without cramping or injuring the working parts. By elevating the feeding apparatus to its highest position, the machine can be used, if desired, as a hand feed band ripping saw. The saw blade furnished is 22½ feet long, 3″ wide, 20 gauge, which furnishes a large amount of cutting surface, and, the blade being thin, removes a very small amount of stock.

THE TIGHT AND LOOSE PULLEYS are 20″ diameter, 6″ face, and should run 500 rotations per minute. The loose pulley is fitted with bronze bearings and a self-oiling device, and is equipped with a convenient belt shipping apparatus, which is operated from the working side of the machine.

HORSE POWER to drive, 5; floor space occupied, 70″ × 75″.

No. 3 Patent Heavy Hand-Feed Ripping Saw.

Net Weight, 1,500 Pounds.

THIS ENGRAVING represents our No. 3 Patent Heavy Hand-Feed Ripping Saw, intended for either light or heavy ripping in hard or soft wood, taking a 24″ saw at the largest, which will saw through material 10″ thick and under. The fence can be adjusted from 0 to 20″ from the saw for sawing lumber of different widths. It is especially intended for heavy ripping such as required in hard wood mills, car and railroad shops, wagon and agricultural implement works, where the principal sawing is in hard wood.

THE COUNTER is furnished as follows: Shaft, $2\frac{3}{16}″ \times 48″$; two No. 2 ball and socket adjustable drop hangers; driving pulley, $30″ \times 8″$; tight and loose pulleys, $14″ \times 8″$; speed, 600 turns per minute; pulley on arbor, $10″ \times 8″$; speed, 1,800 rotations per minute. Also a convenient rack and pinion adjustable belt shifter is furnished.

HORSE POWER to drive, 4; floor space occupied, $58″ \times 72″$.

Defiance 1904 Catalog 194

No. 8 Variety Sawing, Shaping and Boring Machine.

Net Weight, 1,450 Pounds.

Defiance 1910 Catalog 200

No. 1 Improved Trimming Saw.

Net Weight, 800 Pounds.

THIS ENGRAVING represents a new trimming saw designed to meet all the requirements for fine and accurate sawing, chamfering, beveling, trimming off, cutting boards to exact lengths, and it is recommended for wagon and carriage manufacturers, box, furniture, sash, door, moulding, piano, and organ factories.

THE FRAME is of neat design and cast in one piece.

THE TABLE, of iron, in one piece, is 24″ × 41″; the top is planed true and provided with two T shaped slots, one on each side, running the entire length, by which to secure and adjust the fence.

THE SAW ARBOR is $1\frac{5}{13}$″ diameter, forged steel, and it is fitted to a traveling carriage running in genuine babbitt metal self-oiling bearings.

THE ADJUSTABLE IRON FENCE is planed true and square and it can be quickly adjusted to any angle with the saw. A hard wood gauge 60″ long, laid off to inches and fractions, with an adjustable stop, is also furnished; it is used when cutting off material to exact lengths, and when in use it is screwed to the face of the iron fence and is adjustable with it.

THE OPERATION of this machine is very simple; the material is placed upon the table against the fence, the saw is then drawn to the work. The ease and firmness with which the saw works, and the material to be operated upon remaining stationary, insure accurate work. For fine and rapid sawing it has no equal. The greatest distance between the saw and fence is 24″.

THE TIGHT AND LOOSE PULLEYS are 7″ × 4″; speed, 1,400 rotations per minute; pulley on arbor, $3\frac{1}{2}$″ × 3″; speed, 3,400 revolutions per minute.

HORSE POWER to drive, 2; floor space occupied, 40″ × 60″.

Defiance 1904 Catalog 194

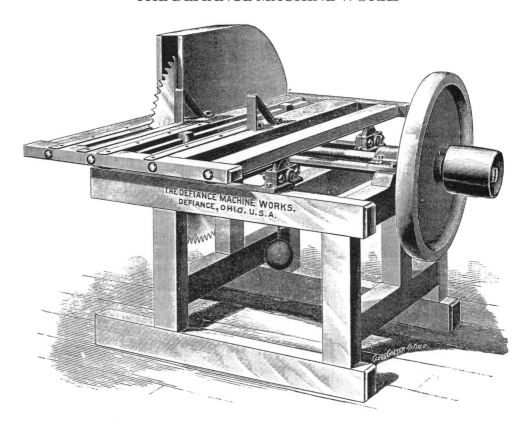

No. 1 Portable Cord Wood Cut-Off Saw.

Net Weight, 400 Pounds.

THIS ENGRAVING represents an improved cut-off saw, used for reducing cord wood, poles, rails, etc., into stove wood lengths. It is also used to prepare the material for pulp and excelsior mills, etc. It will be found a very complete and desirable machine for the purpose intended.

THE SAW ARBOR, of steel, is $1\frac{11}{16}''$ diameter, and runs in babbitt metal self-oiling bearings, which are connected together to keep them in alignment. The outer end of the arbor is fitted with a balance wheel, 24″ diameter, 2½″ face; it is turned true and accurately balanced; the distance between the saw and balance wheel is 36″.

THE SAW is 30″ diameter, and it will cut off material 12″ in thickness; it is covered with a shield when the table is moved back, so the operator cannot become injured.

THE TABLE rides upon friction rollers and moves with the greatest ease; it is supplied with a balance weight to automatically pull the table towards the operator after each cut, which saves time and labor, and keeps the saw under the shield when not in use.

THE PULLEY on the arbor is 6″ × 6″; speed, 1,200 rotations per minute.

HORSE POWER to drive, 3; floor space occupied, 48″ × 48″.

Defiance 1904 Catalog 194

No. 2 Patent Heavy Swing Saw.

Net Weight, 1,900 Pounds.

see next page

No. 2 Patent Heavy Swing Saw.

THIS ENGRAVING represents our Patent No. 2 Extra Heavy Swing Cut-Off Saw, which is adapted to carry a saw from 24″ up to 48″ diameter. It is capable of cutting off heavy lumber or timber, and cutting round logs to lengths suitable for converting same into hub, spoke, wagon, stave, and hoop stock.

IT IS furnished with side brackets to be suspended from the side of a wall, as shown by the engraving, or with connected hangers to fasten to the ceiling, similar to our No. 1 machine, and it is built in seven different lengths, to measure 8 feet, 9 feet, 10 feet, 11 feet, 12 feet, 13 feet, and 14 feet, from the center of the arbor to the top of the hanger.

THE FRAME is cast in one piece with cored center, making it very stiff and reliable; and it is hinged to the hanger, which prevents end wear of the hinged bearings and lateral motion to the frame.

THE SAW ARBOR, of steel, is $1\frac{11}{16}$″ diameter, running in self-oiling, genuine babbitt metal bearings, and it is driven by an 8″ belt; the saw is covered with a shield to protect the operator.

THE PATENT SPRING BALANCES used on this machine for the purpose of pulling the saw back from the operator, out of harm's way, commend special attention; the weighted balances in common use are seriously objectionable, because of their great inertia and consequent resistance at both extremes of swing; it is to overcome this objection that we use the spring balances, and we find their qualities to be incomparable; the adjustments, by which a greater or less tendency backward can be secured, is another desirable feature.

THIS MACHINE is so constructed that the operator is not obliged to lift a weight in pulling the saw forward, at the same time the saw is self-returning.

THE ROLLER TABLE can be furnished to any length required; the rolls are fitted with finished steel spindles running in bored ball and socket boxes, and the lumber can be moved over the table with the greatest ease.

THE COUNTER is a portion of the machine, and it is furnished with belt shipping apparatus; the driving pulley is 24″ diameter, 8″ face; tight and loose pulleys are 14″ diameter, 8″ face; speed, 340 rotations per minute; pulley on arbor, 8″ × 8″; speed, 1,020 revolutions for 36″ saw. In ordering give length from top of hanger to center of saw arbor, also size of saw.

HORSE POWER to drive, 4.

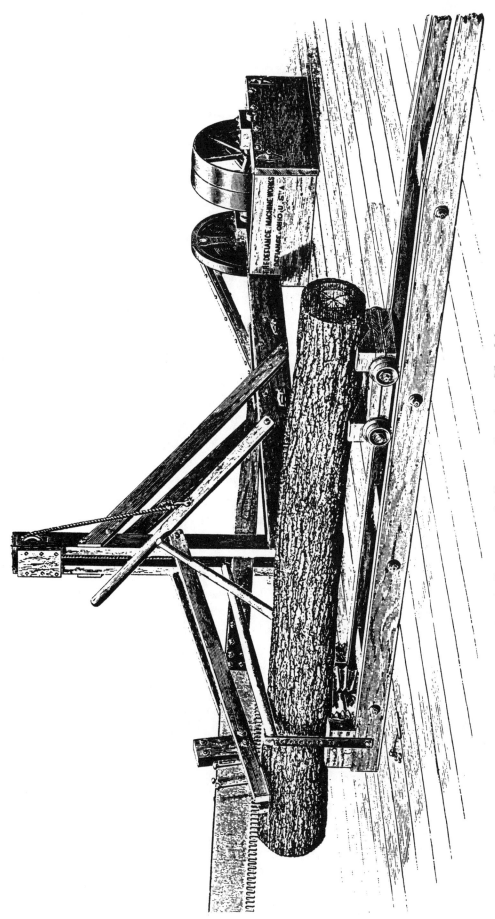

No. 1 Improved Drag Sawing Machine.

Net Weight, 2,100 Pounds.

see next page

No. 1 Improved Drag Sawing Machine.

THIS ENGRAVING represents our No. 1 Improved Drag Sawing Machine, especially designed for cutting off logs of small or large diameters, either hard or soft wood, to different lengths. It is an extremely profitable machine for the makers of hubs, spokes, shafts, poles, rims, hoops, staves, heading, and other manufacturers who purchase their material in the log.

THE FRAME is constructed of heavy timbers bolted together and well braced to stand the heavy labor expected of it.

THE DRIVING POWER is placed between substantial bearings. The shaft is $2\frac{15}{16}''$ diameter, and the balance wheel forming the crank to which the connecting rod attaches, weighs 350 pounds, and the sliding cross-head and other working parts are equally durable throughout.

THE SAW is 7 feet long and 10'' wide with teeth to cut both ways. It has a stroke of 28'' and is fitted to the arm between two heavy steel plates so arranged that it can be quickly connected or disconnected. By the use of a convenient hand lever the saw is moved up or down, to or from its work, while the machine is in motion, and it can be locked in position when elevated to the highest point to enable the operator to feed the log forward for the next cut.

THE DOG for holding the log consists of spurs located on each side of the saw, and it follows the saw when lifted from the cut without any attention on the part of the operator.

THE LOG FEEDING DEVICE is fitted on top with a steel track and upon this the log car travels. The track can be continued into the log yard and the car can also be used for hauling the logs to the machine; by this arrangement only one handling of the log is necessary. The ratchet lever used for moving the log is connected to a heavy steel shaft to which are fitted two taper spur wheels upon which the log rests, and they can be moved forward or backward by reversing the ratchet dog, for the purpose of gauging the length of cut.

THIS MACHINE is capable of cutting off a 24'' hardwood log in one-half minute. It will do more work than twelve men with hand saws and do it better.

THE TIGHT AND LOOSE PULLEYS for driving the machine are 36'' diameter, 6'' face, and should run 140 turns per minute.

HORSE POWER to drive, 5; floor space occupied, 156'' × 312''.

Defiance 1904 Catalog 194

No. 5 Wood Frame Short Log Sawmill and Edger.

Net Weight, 2,300 Pounds.

see next page

No. 5 Wood Frame Short Log Sawmill and Edger.

THIS ENGRAVING represents an improved short log sawmill used for sawing short logs into plank suitable for ripping into spoke and handle squares, and preparing them for the turning lathe, or for cutting rim, shaft, pole, and other wagon and carriage stock from the log.

IT IS USUALLY built for spoke and handle factories to cut 4 feet long and shorter, and fitted with a 40″ saw, which covers all the requirements in this line, although it can be furnished to special lengths to carry a 60″ saw, if so ordered. Extra long machines of this kind are generally used as heavy edgers for trimming the edges of heavy hard wood plank.

THE TABLE upon which the material is placed while being operated upon is so constructed that it may be used as a double traveling table, or a single traveling table; when used in the latter manner the bolts are taken out of the cross tie at the rear end, and the back table is held fast by a bolt to form a stationary table to receive the sawed lumber as it falls from the saw. The use of the tables as a double traveling table is for halving or quartering logs and splitting square timber.

THE FRICTION FEED for operating the table is noiseless, and of the most rapid and positive kind, with two changes for speed from 90 feet to 100 feet per minute; it has a self-reverse at the end of the stroke, or it can be instantly reversed or stopped at any point by a slight movement of the vertical hand lever, as shown.

THE SAW ARBOR is made of hammered steel, $2\frac{7}{16}$″ diameter, with saw end reduced to 2″ diameter and provided with wrought iron saw collars, fitted with two ⅝″ steel dowel pins in a 4″ circle to hold the saw.

THE ARBOR BOXES are cast together in the form of a heavy bed plate to insure alignment of the bearings, which consist of genuine babbitt metal with the wearing surfaces accurately scraped to fit.

EACH MACHINE is furnished with one patent fence, which is adjustable for ripping material to different thicknesses; or a pair of dogs to grip the log at the ends, so that it can be sawed to any angle to which it may be held.

A 40″ SAW is furnished, and it will cut through material 15½″ thick, although a larger saw, up to 60″, can be used when necessary.

A COUNTER is furnished, when ordered, as follows: Shaft, $2\frac{7}{16}$″ × 72″ long; two No. 4 J drop ball and socket adjustable hangers; two $2\frac{7}{16}$″ slip collars with headless set screws; one belt shipper complete; one driving pulley, 36″ × 10″; tight and loose pulleys, 20″ × 12″; speed, 500 rotations per minute; pulley on saw arbor, 18″ × 10″; speed, 900 rotations per minute, for a 40″ saw.

HORSE POWER to drive, 8; floor space occupied, 72″ × 96″.

Defiance 1904 Catalog 194

No. 14 Improved Post Boring Machine.

Net Weight, 165 Pounds.

Defiance 1910 Catalog 200

THE DEFIANCE MACHINE WORKS

No. 1 Patent Horizontal Boring Machine.

Net Weight, 500 Pounds.

THIS MACHINE will bore holes in hard wood up to 2″ diameter, 7″ deep. It is supplied with four boring augers, wrenches, and a universal chuck that will open to receive from the smallest to ½″ diameter shank.

THE COUNTER is a portion of the machine, and can be belted to from above, below, or either side. Tight and loose pulleys, 8″ × 3″; speed, 1,000 rotations per minute.

HORSE POWER to drive, 1; floor space occupied, 24″ × 48″.

Defiance 1904 Catalog 194

32″ Patent Variety Lathe.

Net Weight, 2,200 Pounds.

see next page

32″ Patent Variety Lathe.

THIS ENGRAVING represents our Patent Variety Lathe especially designed for turning table legs, stair balusters, ball bats, croquet mallets, piano stool posts, Indian clubs, tenpins, and various other shapes of fancy turning, or plain work where exact duplicates and accuracy are required.

THE FRAME is a trunk casting, cored out, making it exceedingly stiff and strong without unnecessary weight. The machine is built in seven different sizes to turn material up to the following lengths: 24″, 32″, 38″, 42″, 48″, 52″, and 58″. These are extreme lengths which the different machines will turn. They, however, will turn anything shorter than the lengths given.

THE SPINDLE is made of forged steel running in genuine babbitt metal bearings made in halves and provided with self-lubricating oil cellars and cups.

THE CUTTER HEADS each carry three knives with their cutting edges shaped to suit the style of work desired to turn. It requires different heads and knives for different styles of work, but with any one set of heads and knives the machine can be adjusted by the use of inexpensive cams for turning the same shape of work in round, oval, hexagon, octagon, and square without any change whatever in the cutters; a moment's time is required to change the machine from any one of the shapes specified.

THE TABLE is operated by a convenient hand lever, and it slides upon planed V-shaped ways and is gibbed to the frame. The table is provided with adjusting screws at each end for regulating the diameter of turning. This can be instantly accomplished and the diameter of turning may be varied from the smallest size up to 8″ diameter; it can be furnished to swing up to 12″ diameter when so ordered. The headstock contains a spur center which is rotated by a belt from the cutter head spindle to a sub-counter, attached to the base of the machine, thence to tight and loose pulleys, which are movable, with the table so arranged that the belt for driving the feed is automatically shifted as the table is moved in and out, rotating the material to be turned as it advances toward the cylinder and stopping it automatically when the table is moved back to the proper position to remove the turned object from the centers after the turning is performed.

THE OPERATION of this machine is quick and simple. The material to be turned is placed between the centers in its rough state, with square corners if desired, and moved to the cutter heads by the hand lever, when it is reduced to its proper diameter and shape its entire length at one and the same time. With the knives kept in proper order the work is turned smooth so that no polishing is required. Sharp corners, small curves, and fine beads can be cut without breaking them down or lifting the fiber.

THE CAPACITY of this machine depends somewhat upon the style of work, varying from 1,000 to 3,000 pieces per day. Round, oval, oblong, square, hexagon, or octagon shapes can be turned with equal success. Samples of the work as shown represent some of the different shapes that can be successfully produced with this machine. Before prices can be quoted for these machines it will be necessary for us to have a full size drawing of the different shapes to be turned.

THE COUNTER is furnished as follows: Shaft, $2\frac{7}{16}$″ diameter; two No. 2 adjustable drop hangers; driving pulley, 30″ × 6″; tight and loose pulleys, 14″ × 6″; speed, 600 rotations per minute; pulley on machine, 8″ diameter, 6″ face.

SAMPLES of work submitted upon application.

HORSE POWER to drive, 4; floor space occupied for 24″ machine, 37″ × 66″; for other sizes add difference only to length of each sized machine.

Defiance 1904 Catalog 194

No. 3 Improved Iron Bed Wood Turning Lathe.

Net Weight, 2,100 Pounds.

see next page

No. 3 Improved Iron Bed Wood Turning Lathe.

IT WILL BE OBSERVED by referring to the accompanying engraving that valuable improvements have been made in the design and construction of wood turning lathes not found in machines of this kind heretofore offered. Pattern makers, furniture builders, and woodworkers in general using machines of this kind expect to perform a fine class of turning, consequently the best machines must be employed in order to obtain satisfactory results. We are offering in this lathe a neatness of design, good workmanship, and conveniences that are worthy of careful consideration.

THE BED is ten feet in length, made heavy and deep. It is cast in one piece, with cored center, planed true and finished over the entire upper surface. The outside edges are neatly rounded, while the inner shoulders forming the opening in which the tail stock slides are planed square and parallel, making a neat fit to allow the tail stock to be moved over the bed without cramping, and at all times the head and tail centers will stand in alignment with each other.

THE HEAD SPINDLE, of heavy hammered steel, runs in large split bronze bearings provided with self-oiling devices. The cone pulley attached to it, of iron, has three steps for various changes of speeds. They are 8″, 10″, and 12″ diameter, for 3″ belt. It is balanced by our centrifugal balancing machine to a perfect running balance for all changes of speed. The front end of the spindle is provided with a screw face-plate and a plain face-plate and the regular equipment of centers. The rear end is provided with a plain face-plate for holding large and small circles. A neat and convenient adjustable floor stand is furnished for the support of the tool, and it is of sufficient weight to stand firm. The upper portion is provided with a swivel for securing a delicate adjustment to or from the work.

THE TAIL SPINDLE can be quickly moved to or from the head spindle by loosening a single screw for short or long work, and it is provided with a cup and taper center.

THIS MACHINE is built in two sizes to swing 20″ and 24″ diameter. It can, however, be furnished to swing larger work if so ordered. It is provided with one each 6″, 12″, and 48″ tool rests, and the necessary oil cups and wrenches.

THE COUNTER is furnished as follows: Shaft, $1\frac{11}{16}″ \times 40″$; two No. 1 ball and socket adjustable drop hangers, complete with belt shifting apparatus; one three-step cone pulley, 8″, 10″, and 12″, for 3″ belt; the tight and loose pulleys are $10″ \times 4″$; speed, 1,000 revolutions per minute.

HORSE POWER to drive, 1; floor space occupied, $26″ \times 156″$.

Defiance 1904 Catalog 194

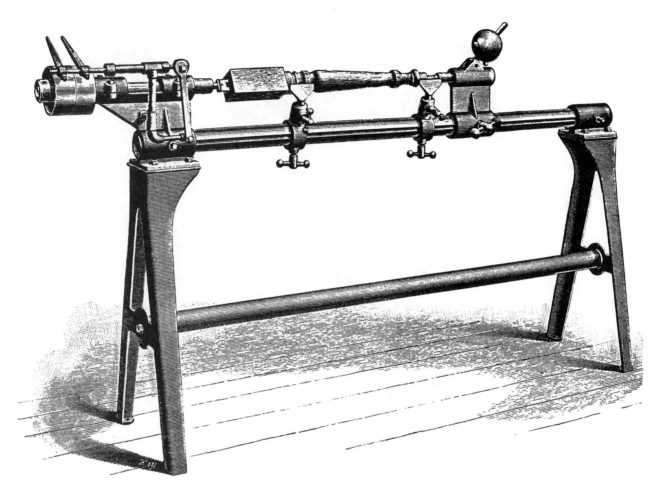

No. 1 Improved Turning and Polishing Lathe.

Net Weight, 300 Pounds.

THE ACCOMPANYING ENGRAVING represents an Improved No. 1 Wood Turning and Polishing Machine used by pattern makers, furniture builders, handle and neck-yoke manufacturers, etc., for turning and polishing woodwork of various kinds within its capacity.

IT IS built in different lengths to suit the purchaser, and will swing 9½" diameter and under. The entire machine is composed of metal with all the parts accurately fitted.

THE COUNTER is a portion of the machine; the tight and loose pulleys are 5" diameter, 2" face, and should run 2,500 rotations per minute.

HORSE POWER to drive, ⅛; floor space occupied, 18" × 82".

Defiance 1904 Catalog 194

No. 2 Improved 24″ Horizontal Drum and Disc Sandpapering Machine.

Net Weight, 1,400 Pounds.

THIS MACHINE is recommended for the use of wagon, carriage, agricultural implement, furniture, and other manufacturers of woodwork. It will polish flat stock up to 24″ wide. By removing the tables, which requires but a moment's time, the polishing drum is exposed, and it can then be used for polishing bent stock and irregular work.

THE TIGHT AND LOOSE PULLEYS are 12″ diameter, 4″ face, and should run 1,000 rotations per minute.

HORSE POWER to drive, 2; floor space occupied, 36″×64″.

Defiance 1904 Catalog 194

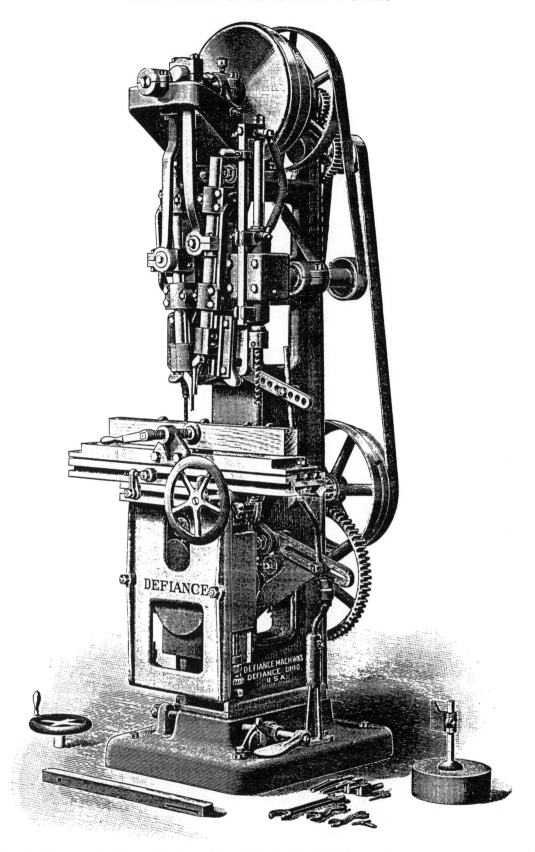

No. 6 Patent Automatic Double Chisel Mortising and Boring Machine.

Net Weight, 2,000 Pounds.

see next page

No. 6 Patent Automatic Double Chisel Mortising and Boring Machine.

THIS MACHINE, as shown by the accompanying engravings, represents a Patent No. 6 Automatic Double Chisel Mortising and Boring Machine, designed for rapidly and accurately cutting mortises in either hard or soft wood from ⅛″ up to 1½″ wide, and from ⅛″ to 6″ long, such as required in wagon, carriage, furniture, agricultural, and other shops.

THE FRAME is very large and heavy, with the driving power at the top. It has two chisel bars arranged side by side upon the front of the column, their axis being on a vertical plane at right angles to the axis of the main shaft.

THE BORING APPARATUS is contained within an iron case which completely covers the gears, and so constructed that the center of the auger is always exactly in line with the center of the chisels, so that the object after being bored has only to be moved laterally to bring it in proper place under the chisels, to receive the mortise. The boring spindle can be used as a separate boring machine when not required for mortising.

THE TABLE on which the timber rests has a screw clamp for holding the work. It has a longitudinal and transverse (right angular) adjustment for regulating the position of the mortise to be made. The bed upon which the table rests is gibbed to the front of the main frame, and is elevated to the chisels by a lifting cam operating on a friction roller.

THE TIMBER TO BE MORTISED is clamped in a vise and it is automatically presented to the action of the chisels by a vertical movement of the bed; when a mortise is cut it descends by its own gravity.

THE OPERATOR has complete control over the machine from the working side; the friction clutch at the top of the machine is connected by foot lever. The weight of the operator's foot upon the lever instantly starts the chisel bars, and the table carrying the work to be mortised is gradually lifted to the chisels until the full depth of cut is reached, where it remains stationary until the mortise is completed, when it descends ready for the next mortise, the feeding being entirely automatic.

IT WILL CUT 6,000 medium sized mortises in soft wood in ten hours, without a variation in the dimensions of the mortises of $\frac{1}{100}$″ from a specific measurement. It will make mortises tapering in either direction, or parallel, as desired, or tapering at one end and perpendicular to the surface at the other end. No painstaking, difficult, and uncertain gigging of a carriage is required, and no reversing of chisels.

THE RECEIVING PULLEY on the machine is 16″ diameter, 3″ face, and should run 370 turns per minute. The pulley on the main line by which it is driven should have a 3″ face.

HORSE POWER to drive, 2; floor space occupied, 36″×36″.

Defiance 1904 Catalog 194

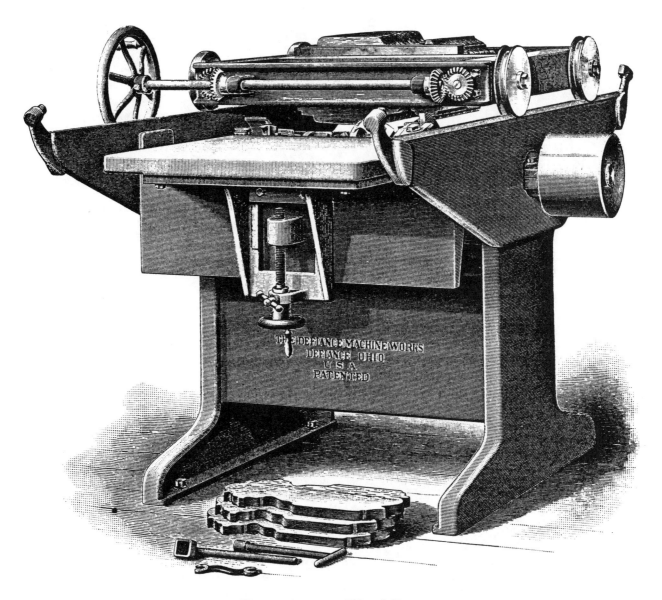

Patent Transverse Moulding Machine.

Net Weight, 2,000 Pounds.

see next page

Patent Transverse Moulding Machine.

THIS ENGRAVING represents a new Transverse Moulding Machine designed for cutting mouldings upon the edge of short boards, corner blocks, etc., as shown by the accompanying engravings representing samples of work.

THIS MACHINE is used by the manufacturers of furniture, desks, sewing machine woodwork, pianos, organs, etc., where a large number of duplicate parts of this kind are required. Previous to its introduction this work was performed upon scroll or band saws; it being a slow process and requiring the marking out of work before sawing and the finishing by hand to remove the saw marks before completion.

ALL THIS is now accomplished by the use of the Transverse Moulder so smooth that no hand labor is required, and 100,000 pieces can be made to exact size and shape, and laying off the work is avoided, with a capacity equal to that of twenty scroll saws.

THE FRAME is a heavy casting with cored center, having a broad floor support; the top forms two parallel tracks which are accurately planed and upon which the carriage travels.

THE TRAVELING CARRIAGE is fitted with a sliding jaw, forming a large chuck which accurately clamps and holds the material in position while being operated upon.

THE CUTTER HEADS are fitted to a 2¼″ steel spindle, which is located in the center of the main frame underneath the traveling carriage, and the heads are supplied with knives of the shape desired to cut; a table, having a vertical adjustment by hand wheel and screw, is located immediately in front of the cutters for securing alignment to the work to be gripped by the chuck and gauge the depth of cut.

IN OPERATION the carriage is first moved over the table, and the stock to be planed is placed between the jaws of the carriage, and rests upon the table; the jaws are then closed and the material clamped into position by turning the hand-wheel attached to the carriage; the carriage with its contents is then moved over the cutter heads by hand and the work completed; when the end of cut is reached the jaws are released and the entire contents of the chuck are discharged. The chuck when wide open measures 24″ long × 25″ wide, and it is capable of receiving 24 boards 1″ thick, 25″ long, all of which can be operated upon at one time; other pieces of different sizes and shapes can be worked in proportion.

THIS MACHINE is built in special large sizes to order, with heads and knives for cutting almost any class of edge moulding.

THE COUNTER is furnished as follows: Shaft, 48″ long, 2³⁄₁₆″ diameter; journals, 1⅛″ diameter; two No. 2 ball and socket hangers; driver, 30″ × 6″; tight and loose pulleys, 14″ × 6″; speed, 600 rotations per minute; pulley on machine, 8″ × 6″; speed, 2,250 rotations per minute.

HORSE POWER to drive, 3; floor space occupied, 54″ × 72″.

Defiance 1904 Catalog 194

Chapter 4

THE OLIVER MACHINERY COMPANY

"Quality Our Watchword"

The Oliver Machinery Company can trace its roots back to the American Machinery Company, founded in Grand Rapids, Michigan, in 1890 by Joseph W. Oliver.

Oliver was born in Oswego, New York, in 1864 and moved to Grand Rapids in 1878 at the age of 14. He became an apprentice machinist at the Bissell Carpet Sweeper Company and later at Butterworth & Lowe Co., which originally made wood trimmers. (Oliver Machinery Co. would buy out Butterworth & Lowe years later.)

The first wood trimmer was made in 1879 at Middletown, Connecticut, and patented by W.R. Fox. Fox took out additional patents on the tool in 1885 and began manufacturing The Fox Universal Trimmers in Grand Rapids. A wood trimmer, sometimes called a miter trimmer or a universal wood trimmer, stands midway between a hand tool and a power machine. Hand or foot activated, two razor-sharp knives, operating somewhat like a guillotine in a cast iron frame, offer controlled shaving of stock. An end that would take from 10 to 15 minutes to square and true up by hand with a square and plane or chisel, can be finished in as many seconds. It is used mainly by patternmakers and for cutting picture frame moldings where precision is mandatory.

Oliver left Butterworth & Lowe and became a salesman for The Fox Machine Co. Then, utilizing his skills as a trained machinist and his practical experience of what customers were looking for, he designed his own trimmer and persuaded the local Perkins Machine Co. to build and market it.

The Perkins-Oliver relationship did not last long. In 1890, certain he could do better marketing his own trimmers, Oliver designed a new and more advanced line. Having no facilities of his own, he farmed out the actual manufacturing to various Grand Rapids companies that made woodworking machinery, such as Baldwin, Tuthill & Bolton, and The C. O. Porter Machine Co., which made the smaller models.

By 1891 the Builders Iron Foundry, Providence, Rhode Island, was manufacturing the machines for Oliver's company, now called The American Machinery Company. The wood trimmer line consisted of Nos. 1, 2, and 3; employees numbered two, and stockholders one – Joseph Oliver.

The company's catalog No. 21 (ca. 1921), though appearing 30 years later, still offered and described these trimmers. The line consisted of ten models, from the No.0 Small to the No.10 Full Universal.

In 1892 the company moved to Detroit, where the (Henry M.) Leland Machine Works (later Cadillac Motor Co.) was contracted to build the American trimmers. In 1896 Oliver made a personal tour of pattern shops all over England, Ireland, and Scotland, demonstrating trimmers and selling them from a flamboyant custom-painted horse-drawn lorry.

By 1898 Oliver, tiring of the headache of jobbing the work out, decided it was high time American built the trimmers itself; he opened the company's first factory in a basement shop. Business increased and in 1900 Oliver moved into an old factory building.

American exhibited its machines at the 1900 World's Fair in Paris, where the company won a highest award gold medal for merit. One machine on exhibit was American's new Universal Saw Bench (tablesaw). According to Oliver, Mr. White of Thomas White & Sons Co., a large English woodworking machinery manufacturer, came into the booth and, patting the table of the saw, said, "Well, I've copied this machine in every detail — what else do you have to show me?"

In 1902 American began expanding its own line of machines with the addition of its Universal Saw Bench (made by Oliver), which would evolve into the No.60 Saw Bench. It also carried a jointer made by C. Oscar Porter. The soon-to-be-listed bandsaws were made by the West Side Iron Works.

In 1903 it was decided that the company's name needed to be changed, since it was being confused with the huge American Wood Working Machinery Co. of Rochester, New York, a major competitor. "The Oliver Machinery Co." was chosen. Trimmers, however, continued to bear "Made By American Machinery Co." for some time.

Employees in 1903 numbered about 25. The average hourly wage was 17¢ an hour for a 60 hour week. That same year Oliver moved into an even larger factory.

Oliver raised more capital in 1904 and began the development of new machinery for pattern-making. In that year the company also printed its first real catalog. Called catalog A, it was an ostentatious but important effort. It bore the title "The Oliver Machinery Company, successors to the American Machinery Co." The company trademark, the spread American eagle with the new and old worlds, appeared on the cover. (The company still uses the trademark on all its literature, stationery, name plates, etc.).

Oliver determined that a further expansion was needed, and by 1906 the company had completed building its own new factory, which had over 60,000 square feet of floor space. (A ca. 1921 catalog describes the plant as covering 102,000 square feet and surrounded by 50 acres of public parks.) The company was incorporated January 7, 1907, with capital consisting of $100,000 in common shares and $50,000 in preferred stock. The net worth of the company was listed as $436,152 on October 1, 1907. Still working 60 hour weeks, the average Oliver worker earned 21¢ per hour.

Oliver began putting serial numbers on its machinery in 1907. Serial Number 1 went on a Type B tablesaw (the forerunner of the No.60 tablesaw) which was sold to the J.L. Todd Lumber Co. of Tacoma, Washington, and shipped August 17, 1907. (As a point of reference, the serial number of the first machine shipped after January 1, 1990 was 207675.)

Other Oliver machines offered by 1907 included bandsaws, the Universal Trimmer, pattern-maker's lathes, and a jointer. A photo of one lathe clearly shows the legend "'The Oliver' American Machinery Co." cast into the frame, illustrating how the original molds were reworked into Oliver machines.

Oliver has often been first in the field. It offered the first motor head speed lathe and unit type motor headstocks, the first with a motor armature on the lower shaft of a bandsaw, and many others.

Perhaps the greatest innovation in woodworking machinery, including the replacement of babbitt bearings with ball bearings and line shafts by electric motors, was the introduction of the round cutterhead. The head was first developed in England (1901) and later in Germany, where it was patented January 21, 1908. Oliver purchased the German patent the same year. Every circular safety cylinder in the United States today is basically a copy of the one brought out by Oliver.

The Grand Rapids Furniture Record (May 1910) wrote: "The Oliver Machinery Company were the first American makers of machinery to market a cutting cylinder for use in a hand planer (jointer) that would save the operator's fingers and hand from serious mutilation. Although the invention is not more than two years old, 2000 of them are in use in this country and over 4000 in Europe."

The knives projected so little from the head that if an operator's hand did slip and come in contact with the knives, it would not be horribly mangled as it was by a square head (see p. 105). An accident on the old type would cost several fingers. A slip with the new type would cost only some fingertips. The safety features were so apparent – changing an extremely dangerous machine into one of near-perfect safety – that many states soon began requiring their installation. Insurance companies also began to insist upon it.

Though the round cutterhead was originally invented to prevent serious accidents, its side benefits were less noise, less vibration, efficient use of power, and smoother surfacing.

Machines equipped with square cutterheads, particularly jointers, had to allow a large gap in the table so the head could revolve freely. Used in a jointer, the round head presented a regular smooth surface and filled the wide gap caused by the separation of the tables, thus preventing fingers getting below the table top between the cutter and the table edges.

Along with round jointer and planer cutterheads, Oliver specialized in making similar heads for matchers, molders, shapers, etc., with either two or four knives. Oliver would also custom machine a safety head to fit another manufacturer's planer or jointer – any diameter, any length, any size hole. Every cylinder was guaranteed to be flaw free.

In June 1909 the company made an extra effort to expand sales beyond pattern shops, targeting the growing number of furniture-making factories and other woodworking plants. Part of this new direction was the development of swing cut-off saws, spindle sanders, and vertical boring machines. Though a success mechanically, the spindle sander was never a good seller. The company, in 1908, had purchased manufacturing rights to the wood milling machine invented by Joseph Williams Wadkins of Wadkins & Co., Leicester, England. In addition, in July 1910 Oliver announced in various trade papers that it was bringing out its own wood milling machine.

The Oliver work week had shrunk to 55 hours by 1912, with an average wage of 22¢ an hour. Annual sales in 1913 approached $230,000 (by 1949 this was considered a poor month's income!). July 1914 was the best month to that date, bringing in $47,000 in orders.

During the first World War, Oliver's sales of woodworking machinery to naval yards, arsenals, and other U.S. government installations increased. The company developed a line of metalworking engine lathes for the war effort, introducing the line in 1915. Over 1000 of them were sold by 1920. In 1919-20 the demand for woodworking machinery increased so much that Oliver dropped the engine lathe line to concentrate on woodworking machinery.

On December 31, 1919, Oliver Machinery, now owned by V.M. Tuthill and F.A. and R.F. Baldwin, purchased the owners' own company – Baldwin, Tuthill & Bolton – factory, inventory, and equipment. In other words, the companies merged, becoming the Oliver Machinery Co. The title "Oliver" was retained, since it was a well established and respected name.

In 1920 Oliver exported $213,764 worth of machinery and accessories to 30 foreign countries, representing 21.3% of its sales that year.

Like those of all machinery manufacturers, Oliver's first machines were flat belt driven, with self-oiling high speed babbitt bearings. The company later offered accurately finished replacement sleeve bearings to avoid re-babbitting and eventually switched completely to ball bearings and electric drives.

Catalog No.21 (1921) listed some 48 basic woodworking machinery models. Only eight machines had ball bearings; the remaining forty had babbitt, bronze, or sleeve bearings.

What a difference a year can make! Catalog No. 22 of 1922, only one year later, revealed great changes. The woodworking machinery line was now made up of 68 basic machines, 26 of them new. Forty of the machines from the year before still featured babbitt, bronze, and sleeve bearings, but the remaining 28 had been converted to ball

93

bearings. Missing from the 1921 line were one tablesaw, one swing cut-off saw, one jointer, one lathe, the single end tenoner, and one wood trimmer.

Catalog 22 introduced Oliver's first production double surface planer, the No.169, available in 30" x 8" and 36" x 8" widths with ball and bronze bearings. It also listed Oliver's first ball bearing single end tenoner, the No.125. The old No.37 Swing Cut-Off Saw Table, made from kiln dried rock maple 3" x 4" stock, now had cast iron legs and was designated the No.179.

One unusual wood lathe listed in the 1922 catalog was the No.18-A. Oliver shipped such a machine built for the U.S. Navy on October 7, 1919. Motor driven, it had a 32" swing, a 62' bed, with two power feeding carriages, two steady rests, and a weight of 19,760 pounds! A photo shows 44 men standing behind the monster machine, illustrating why Oliver billed itself as the world's largest manufacturer of wood turning lathes.

Oliver calculated that more than 1500 high, grammar, and intermediate schools with manual training departments used Oliver machinery. Between 1908 and 1922, for example, the Minneapolis Board of Education purchased 264 Oliver machines – 164 lathes, 7 planers, 8 bandsaws, 5 tablesaws, 7 grinders, 48 forges, 2 blowers, 2 exhausters, 8 jointers, 3 mortisers, 1 swing cut-off saw, 1 swing saw table, 2 jigsaws, 2 belt sanders, 2 wood trimmers, and 2 disc sanders. The repeat orders said a lot about the machinery's quality.

In 1922 the company developed a line of junior-sized woodworking machines. Actually, what Oliver did was sort through its large machinery line and select those machines it deemed suitable for home shop use and light production work. These were then gathered together and, in a smart advertising move, promoted as a separate line. All the machines would run off household current.

Catalog No.24, second edition, of Oliver Junior Line Woodworking Machinery (ca.1922) listed eight machines plus a band saw brazer, vises, clamps, glue pots, and heaters.

Also in 1922, deciding that resources were being spread too thin over two lines of machinery, the company took advantage of a chance to sell Baldwin, Tuthill & Bolton's line of saw sharpening and saw swaging equipment to Hanchett Manufacturing Co. of Grand Rapids and the Covell Manufacturing Co. of Benton Harbor. Oliver, for the time being, would concentrate on woodworking machinery.

In 1923, Oliver was approached by the Widdicomb Furniture Co. of Grand Rapids and asked if it could supply a machine that could quickly surface, straighten, and plane to thickness badly warped and twisted stock. Oliver's engineering staff went to work. The resulting machine was the first of its kind. Marketed as the Straitoplane, the first one was delivered to Widdicomb the same year. The machine, occasionally modernized, is still being sold.

The Straitoplane is a combination planer and jointer that can actually plane a warped board perfectly flat and straight on both surfaces in one pass. A feeding system, consisting of a series of cams over the infeed table, "pushes" the board through the machine. Like hand feeding a board over a jointer, where the fingers can not exert enough force to flatten out the warp as feed rolls do, the cams do not flatten the board yet hold it securely in place no matter what its shape. For example, if the board is warped so that when one end is held down flat the other end is raised 1/4", the cams will hold the board so that each end is raised 1/4" above the table. Therefore a 1/4" cut will completely level the underside of the board.

After the board passes the jointer cutterhead, it goes through a single surfacer placed over the outfeed table, where it is planed on top and exits the machine perfectly straight and planed true on both surfaces.

In 1929 the company took in 9406 orders. It also bought the Eaglesfield-Link Co., which manufactured a small 4" electric molder.

The Depression did not hurt Oliver immediately, but eventually sales began to slacken. By 1931 Oliver was suffering. The bottom was hit in

1932 and 1933; business had fallen off by 92%! By the close of 1933 the net worth of the company had fallen about 45%. More losses were to come. Only good pre-Depression business practices saved the company from bankruptcy. Workers were earning 50¢ an hour and scraping by on 30 hour work weeks (when work was even available).

Though hurt by the Depression, Oliver managed to hold on. It was clear however that Oliver had to diversify. The first effort was a modified No.192 band saw for meat cutting. It was a failure.

It was at this time that Oliver developed a small bread slicing machine designed for neighborhood bakeries. The first was sold to the Polly Anna Bakery of Grand Rapids. Perhaps borrowing a page from Joseph Oliver's book, female Oliver employees would go to other bakeries asking for sliced bread. When told it wasn't available, the women would say they could get it at Polly Anna's. From this tiny beginning grew a thriving worldwide business.

The simple slicing machine led to a large and complex line of machinery whose manufacture was concentrated at Oliver's West Side plant (the old Baldwin, Tuthill & Bolton plant).

Naturally the bread slicing machine was followed by a bread wrapping machine. The first was a handwrapping machine; it was followed by more intricate machines that could package almost anything.

Of course most packages had to be labeled — especially all food crossing state lines. The company pursued this business as well. Not only were machines designed to prepare labeling material and attach labels, but Oliver would print labels as well.

Oliver developed the roll type, thermoplastic (heat-seal) paper label in collaboration with the Grand Rapids Label Co., which printed the labels for the Oliver labeling machine that accompanied its packaging machinery. Oliver later went on to design and supply labelers for other manufacturers' packaging equipment.

Oliver gradually emerged from the Depression, overcoming a sudden recession in 1937 and a small dip in sales in 1944 and 1945. The net worth of the company in 1941 was calculated at $566,438, a bit less than it had been in 1922. By 1941, the average Oliver worker earned 77¢ an hour for a 45 hour work week.

In 1947 the company's woodworking machinery line included bandsaws such as the 30" No.217, boring machines, carving machines, tablesaws such as the No.270 tilting arbor, cut-off saws, jigsaws, jointers, metal spinning lathes, mortisers, sanders, shapers, planers, tenoners, wood trimmers, and lathes. "Every User Is A Booster," read an ad from that year.

Oliver calculated in 1950 that its machinery was being used in over 2200 vocational shops. The machine line had basically remained the same, with such models as the No.159 Motor Driven Speed Lathe and the No.194-B vertical single spindle borer.

In that year, Oliver employed a total of 500 people, about 200 of whom were engaged in building woodworking machinery, earning $1.77 per hour for a 40 hour week. The company was particularly well known for its line of pattern shop equipment, including wood millers, lathes, and the Straitoplanes.

By the end of 1950 the net worth of the company had grown to $2,000,992. About 150 machines were made, not including variations. Employment was 415. Gross sales were $4,642,570.

Oliver had first entered the metal cutting field in 1948. Douglas Aircraft needed a saw to cut aluminum; Oliver therefore modified the wood cutting No.88 tablesaw with its rolling table into the No.88 DM (The No.88 Douglas Modification). The company went on to design other saws for cutting aluminum, brass, copper, mild steel, alloy steel, and even titanium.

In the late 1950s and the 1960s Oliver entered the metal working business in a serious way. Though common wisdom said that you could not cut steel with a carbide tipped saw blade, Oliver engineers proved otherwise. They were the first to cut steel plate with a circular blade. Oliver went on to create an extensive line of metal sawing machinery.

In the mid 1970s, Oliver patented the innovative Model 2694 Wood Opti-Mising Saw. Slightly ahead of its time in the 70s, when it was joined with the computer technology of the early 1990s, the saw really came into its own.

The Model 2694 Opti-Mising Saw, available in 8" or 18" cutting widths, is a computer controlled saw capable of performing the work of three or four manual chop saws. After lumber defects are marked by the operator, the machine looks at the bill of materials and selects the proper lengths for cutting to fill the list with the least amount of waste. Different bills of materials can also be selected based on the width of the incoming lumber. The computer offers many printed reports to provide increased shop floor control; it also provides self-diagnostics to reduce downtime.

In 1981 Oliver sold its packaging and printing machine product line to concentrate on sawing machinery for the worldwide metalworking industry and a full line of production woodworking machinery.

Through the years Oliver has dropped and added various machines to its product line. By 1986 its once extensive line had been whittled down to some 53 basic machines.

The 1992 catalog offered 35 basic machines. Missing from the catalog were all the wood milling machines, the center planer, the tool grinder, the cut-off saw, the 18" and 20" planers, the v-belt bandsaw, the Nos.2003 and 2004 tablesaws, the No.159 variable speed lathe, and all the pattern maker's lathes with the exception of the Nos.2255-2258 series. However, new to the catalog were the computer-controlled Model 2694 Opti-Mising saw and the Model 494 Auto-Defecting saw, and the No.270-VT tilting arbor saw.

By 1994, the company had produced over 150,000 machines and Oliver estimated that over 75,000 were still in operation on a daily basis worldwide. The original quality of the machines and the availability of parts and service was the secret. The Grand Rapids plant maintained $2,000,000 worth of replacement parts. Oliver offered such services as accepting trade-ins of machinery, re-building used machinery, on-site service and instruction, and preventive maintenance contracts. Many of the employees in Grand Rapids had over 30 years of experience. Though over 100 years old, Oliver was still modern enough to proudly supply the saw used to cut the ceramic tiles used on the space shuttle.

The company has used many slogans over the years to advertise its fine machinery: "Quality Our Watchword." "Satisfaction Our Guarantee." "Success Our Ambition." "Manufactured and Assembled In U.S.A. By American Craftsmen."

Perhaps the best compliment to its line was made by retired shop teacher Stephen Rose of Tucson, Arizona, who described Oliver's lathes to me as "boy-proof." A true test of durability if there ever was one!

OUR PLANT
102,000 Square Feet of Floor Space, Surrounded by Fifty Acres of Parks.

Oliver 1921 Catalog 21

No. 3 "OLIVER" FULL UNIVERSAL WOOD TRIMMER
"The Master of them all"

No. 3
"Oliver" Full Universal Wood Trimmer

Over 2,000 in Daily Use

General Construction

Our best knowledge gained through years of experience is incorporated in this machine. It is useful, convenient and popular because it not only has large capacity, but will work on the most delicate material with equal facility. It is made like a machine tool.

Principal Features

Among the many features that are wrought into this powerful trimmer we can refer you to the following that have distinctive merit:

Six handle operating wheel, always in reach on small or large work. Can use two handles on the largest pieces.

Gauges are automatically located upon the prominent angles.

Segment graduations for circles from 6" to 72" in diameter.

Adjustable bearings, doubling its life on accurate work.

Entire top swivels on the column or can be held in a fixed position by a lock nut.

Fine Points

Automatic spring knife guards furnish adequate protection at all times.

Faces of both gauges are graduated in inches for cutting positive lengths.

Rack, gear and bearings are protected from shavings and grit.

Cut gear and cut rack eliminate uneven and loose motion.

The bed is long and wide, making a valuable truing table.

Wear to the knives is adequately provided for.

WEIGHT, ETC.

No.	Stroke	Depth of Cut	Superficial Area	Size of Bed	Domestic Weight	Foreign Weight	Cubic Meas'mt
3	20¾"	7½"	135 sq. in.	18"x34"	660 ℔s.	800 ℔s.	24

See preceding pages descriptive of the principal features of this machine.

Extra Knives

Good results are never obtained with dull tools. Nowhere is this more true than in the case of Trimmers. Our advice is to always have one extra set of knives for each machine, which may be kept in condition to replace the pair on the machine, otherwise you are tempted to use dull knives when in haste. An "Oliver" Wood Trimmer will outlast at least three or four pairs of the best knives that can be made.

98

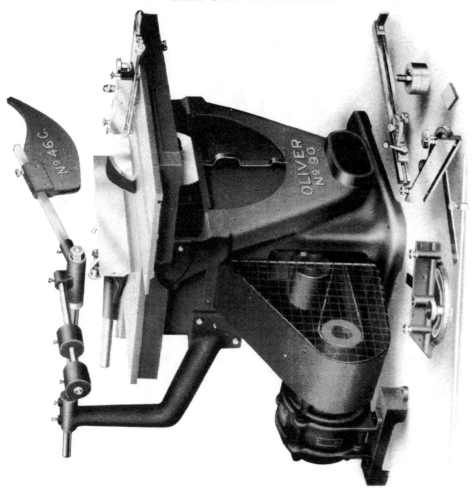

No. 90
"Oliver" Universal Saw Bench

Frame We supply this in the cored form, ribbed for strength, with a wide flange at the base. A metal partition divides the saws from the balance of the working parts and prevents the saw dust from penetrating to them. The side of the frame where the saws are applied is cast to form a natural chute for the saw dust and carries it to the pipe connection at the base. A column guard fills the space opposite lower saw.

Table A metal table of ample proportions is supplied in two sections, one stationary and the other to slide past the saw. It is well ribbed and is very rigid. An extension bracket at the right supports the fence when ripping stock the maximum width. Table tilts to an angle of 45 degrees by means of hand wheel engaging worm and gear.

Sliding Table This is mounted on a tongued cross slide and moves past the saw for use in cutting off and for dado work. The cross slide is gibbed to the main table frame and has provision for drawing 4" away from the saw line, so dado heads and grooving saws may be used. The sliding table will not lift up or tip when drawn to its maximum limit.

Table Graduations The stationary section of the table is graduated its entire width in eighths, and the sliding section is graduated into degrees that cover all the possible acute and obtuse angles.

No. 90 "Oliver" Universal Saw Bench Showing Table Tilted to 30 degrees.

General View of Motor Driven Machine.

This Saw Bench fills a demand for a somewhat smaller machine than our No. 60 Saw Bench. The two principal points of difference being a smaller table top and 14" instead of 16" saws.

The general accuracy of the machine as a whole is apparent in even the smallest detail and for general everyday use, with its various appointments, lends itself to quick change from one class of work to another. The indexing of the gauges, the graduations on top of table, the degree of pitch when the table is tilted are all true; the saws "track right." The gauges will cut square with the saw; it won't run hot and no substitutions of poor for good workmanship or material have been resorted to. It's a quality tool of the "Oliver" kind.

Saw Arbors Two crucible steel machine ground arbors are accurately fitted into bearings that are lined with interchangeable sleeves with oil wells and wick conveyors that keep them flooded with oil continuously. End thrust through wear is taken up by means of a threaded thrust collar drawing the arbor pulley against the end of the bearing. Arbor pulley is of solid steel, machined all over and is of the pneumatic type.

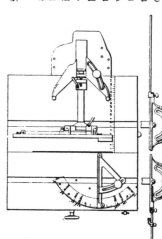

Etching Showing Table Graduations.

99

No. 11
"Oliver" Variety Saw Bench
With Hollow Chisel Mortising and Boring Attachment

"OLIVER" NEW No. 11 VARIETY SAW

General View Showing Universal Miter Gauges and Standard Table with Plain Ripping Fence.

This machine is known as our New Improved No. 11 Variety Saw Bench and Hollow Chisel Mortiser. The new features are the ball bearings, hollow chisel mortiser and boring attachments, worm and gear device for tilting the table, and standardized top to take plain two-sided ripping fence usable on either side of saw.

The No. 11 is a quality machine through and through and strong enough to work up to full capacity on hard woods. Self-locking devices, self-oiling features, fine micrometer adjustment, cut gears and correct workmanship serve to give durability, ease of operation and adjustment.

Base   Is cored one-piece casting, heavy, well-ribbed, and has ample floor support. The rocker seats, which carry the tilting top, are cast solid with the base and properly machined to insure perfect alignment and ease of operation.

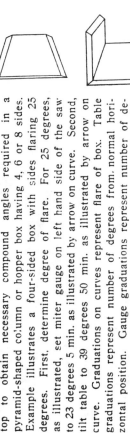

Diagram illustrates method of setting saw gauge and table top to obtain necessary compound angles required in a pyramid-shaped column or hopper box having 4, 6 or 8 sides. Example illustrates a four-sided box with sides flaring 25 degrees. First, determine degree of flare. For 25 degrees, as illustrated, set miter gauge on left hand side of the saw to 23 degrees 5 min. as illustrated by arrow on curve. Second, tilt table to 39 degrees 50 min. as illustrated by arrow on curve. Graduations on curves represent flare of box. Table graduations represent number of degrees from. normal horizontal position. Gauge graduations represent number of degrees from normal position, viz.: 90 degrees from line of saw. Horizontal lines represent gauge graduations. Vertical lines represent table tilting graduations.

No. 45

"Oliver" Hand Feed Rip Saw

Type

This machine has been designed especially for general utility purposes. Its adaptability for either light or heavy work is its main feature. It will be found invaluable in the shops of large industrial institutions where the requirements of a carpenter shop are to take care of every job that comes along whether it is a case of one inch boards, planks or timbers.

Capacity

Will take a saw 26" diameter that will saw to 9" in thickness. An 18" saw projects 5" through the table. Extreme distance between saw and fence, 30".

Table

It is mounted on two cylindrical guides, vertically adjusted by a toggle joint operated by a screw. It has a removable plate at the saw.

Saw Arbor

It is of crucible steel, machine ground and runs in long self-oiling bearings. Arbor pulley is the pneumatic type, giving increased belt contact and power. Where saw is applied the arbor is extended 6", so can rip extra width. Is provided with filling collars.

Fence

This is made of metal, held parallel to the saw. Can be instantly set to graduations and locked by a lever cam.

Guards

Back of the saw we furnish a steel blade splitter or "back guard;" under the table we furnish a removable saw guard; above the table no guard is regularly furnished but "Oliver" No. 46-A Full Automatic Saw Guard with its own floor stand can be furnished when so ordered.

"OLIVER" No. 45 HAND-FEED RIP SAW TABLE
All Guards Removed to Show the Machine.

SPECIAL DATA

Table — 37" x 56", will rise 5½".

Saw Arbor — 1⅜" where saw is applied. Pulley is 7" x 7"; speeds 18" saw 2143 R. P. M. 26" saw 1450 to 1500 R. P. M.

Capacity — Will rip to 21½" wide with saw next to rigid collar, and 26½" wide with saw next to loose collar. 18" saw projects through table 5¼".

Countershaft — Has 10" x 7" T & L pulleys and 20" x 7" drive pulley. Speed 750 R. P. M. for 18" saw. 550 R. P. M. for 26" saw.

Floor Space — With Countershaft—Single, 4' 10" x 8' 3". Double, 6' 0" x 8' 3". Without Countershaft, 3' 8" x 6'.

Horse Power — 6 to 10.

WEIGHT, ETC.

Machine	Domestic Weight	Foreign Weight	Measurement in Cubic Ft.
No. 45-A Machine with one 18" Rip Saw, one ripping fence, saw guard under the table, one splitter guard and countershaft with hangers and pulleys	1600	1800	78
No. 45-B Machine as above except with 26" saw	1700	1900	78

EXTRAS

Countershaft hangers and pulleys omitted when not wanted.
One Endless Leather Belt, to drive saw arbor from countershaft or motor on floor back of machine.
No. 46-A "Oliver" Full Automatic Saw Guard with Floor Stand.
Two-speed countershaft with hangers and pulleys.

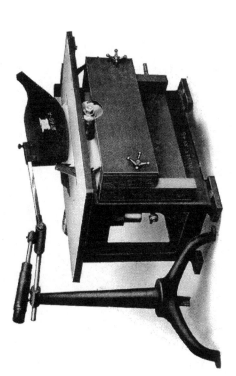

"OLIVER" No. 45 HAND-FEED RIP SAW TABLE
With No. 46-A Saw Guard.

Oliver 1921 Catalog 21

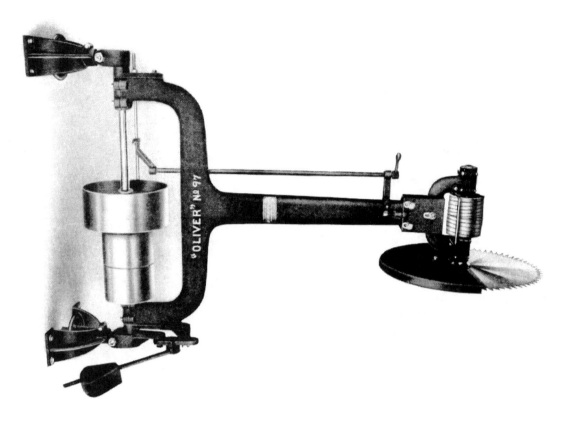

No. 97 "OLIVER" HEAVY SWING CUT-OFF SAW
Fitted for either 36" or 48" Saw.

No. 97
"Oliver" Heavy Swing Cut-Off Saw

Carries Either 36" or 48" Saw

Description   This machine is similar in design to the No. 36 swing cut-off saw, shown on page 30, and differs only in the fact that every part of it is made heavier to meet the needs in using a saw 36" in diameter.

GENERAL DIMENSIONS

Frame   Length between hangers 51".
Length from center of arbor to base of hanger 8'.

**Saw
Arbor**   Length over all 24⅝". Out to out of boxes 20½".
Diameter in bearings 2". Where saw is applied 1½".
Saw Collars 5". Bearings 6" long.
Arbor Pulley 8" x 8½" face. Speed 1125 revolutions per minute.
Adjustment for tightening belt 1".

**Trunnion
Hangers**   Vertical adjustment for keeping saw cutting line 4".

Countershaft   Length 55", diameter 2".
Bearings 6" long.
Hangers 18" drop.
Driving Pulley 20" diameter, 8½" face.
Tight and loose Pulleys 10" diameter, 8½" face.
Speed 450 revolutions per minute.

Horse Power   Maximum 10.

Equipment   We furnish one 36" saw with the No. 97-A machine.
We furnish one 48" saw with the No. 97-B machine.

WEIGHT, ETC.

Machine	Domestic Weight	Foreign Weight	Measurement in Cubic Ft.
No. 97-A 8' long, with 36" saw........1400		1500	86
No. 97-B Same, with 48" saw...........1600		1700	86

EXTRAS

Endless Leather Belt, 8" wide suitable length.
Special Wire Mesh Belt Guard, with supporting brackets.
Wall Brackets in place of Ceiling Brackets.
Motor Bracket Bolted to frame in yoke of machine.

Special quotations made on motor driven machines.

No. 16 "OLIVER" BAND SAW—36-INCH WHEELS
"Oliver" Machines Safely Guarded

No. 16 "Oliver" Band Saw

36-inch Wheels

Our aim has been to produce a medium size of Band Saw embodying the excellent qualities of the No. 15-38" machine. We are correct in our statement that this is the most perfect 36" machine marketed.

Frame It is made in the cored form, is strong, durable and free from vibration when machine is in operation.

Table This is metal, well ribbed and machined, and is mounted in a substantial rocker, that is milled on all surfaces and tongued to its seat and is provided with take up for wear. It tilts either to the right or left by means of a large hand wheel, worm and worm gear self-locking device. It remains at any angle one may put it. It is provided with a device for leveling the top, where it is slotted to receive the saw. A double rib around the edge of the table serves the dual purpose of stiffening it and providing a means for readily clamping forms to table.

Auxiliary Table This is located between the column and main table mounted on a pillar and adjustable vertically, for alignment with main table.

Upper Wheel This is metal and forced on the shaft on a taper bearing and secured by hexagonal nut. It is machined to a running balance. has vertical adjustment and may be tilted for tracking the blade.

Lower Wheel This is metal, fitted to taper bearing and is rigidly held in a fixed position. It is given a running balance.

Bearings These are long, lined with guaranteed babbitt and have ample oil chambers and are made adjustable to wear. The cap joints are machined, and there are milled seats for the bolts, which pass down through the boxes and are held by lock-nuts.

Wheel Shafts They are of fine steel, ground accurately in the journals. Upper shaft is supported in a housing that is provided with devices for regulating the saw tension and for making the blade track on the wheel properly and controlled by hand wheels and screws.

Tension For the saw is regulated by means of a telescope spring. The larger of the two springs regulates the tension for light saws, and when the smaller spring within the large one exerts its resistance, the combined strength gives sufficient pressure for larger saws.

Guide Post Is finished square steel, counterbalanced by an encased coil spring. A very substantial clamping device is provided. The guides are of the frictionless roller type, latest pattern—one above and one beneath the table.

103

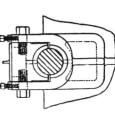

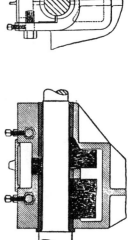

"OLIVER" No. 61 FOUR ROLL, SINGLE CYLINDER, DOUBLE BELTED
CABINET SURFACER
View from Left Hand Side.

Etching Showing Cylinder Bearing on "Oliver" No. 61 Four Roll,
Double Belted, Single Cylinder Surfacer.

No. 61
"Oliver" Single Cylinder Four-Roll Cabinet
Double Belted Surfacer
24 and 30-inch Wide, 8-inch Thick

General Construction
We are constructing these planers along metal tool lines, convinced that in this we are serving our friends properly and satisfactorily. Our success in the past leads us to pursue the same general policy with this surfacer. Only the best of material is used and all parts are individually submitted to thorough tests before using.

Framing
Is of cored sides and heavy ribbed girts, machine jointed and bolted. Ample material in it eliminates the vibration usually communicated through the high speed of the cylinder and the feed mechanism. This material is distributed to properly care for strains.

Cylinder
This is a crucible steel forging of uniform texture, circular in form, carries two thin air hardening, high speed, steel knives, is belted from both ends and revolves in two long bearings that absorb the strain and eliminate rough planing. The steadiness under speed and active service is desirable. The chip breaking lips are shaped to repel the shavings and chips. The journals are long, of large diameter and machine ground. On pages of this catalog will be found a full description of this splendid cylinder.

Circular Cylinder Regularly Furnished with "Oliver" No. 61 Surfacer.

Cylinder Pulleys
These are solid steel, two in number, and perfectly in balance. Their faces are grooved spirally, preventing air pockets under the belts and augmenting the belt power through its close contact with the pulleys.

Cylinder Bearings
Are long, with large oil chambers. They are readily adjusted to hold the cylinder firmly in place for smooth planing. Readjustment of caps made instantly.

Back Pressure Bar
This bar follows the cylinder and is held by adjustable screws for regulating the hold-down pressure on the lumber as it leaves the cut. The throat between the front and rear pressure bars is only 2⅛" for service in planing smooth and without end clipping on very short stock.

104

Oliver 1921 Catalog 21

"Oliver" Circular Safety Cylinder

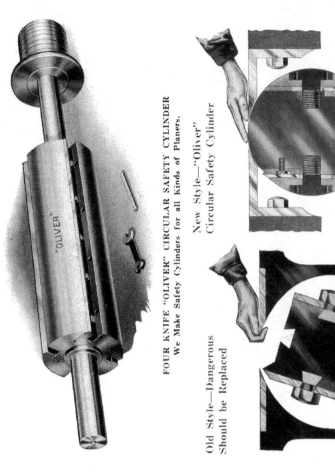

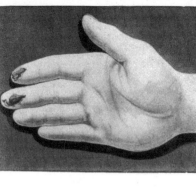

FOUR KNIFE "OLIVER" CIRCULAR SAFETY CYLINDER
We Make Safety Cylinders for all Kinds of Planers.

New Style—"Oliver"
Circular Safety Cylinder

Old Style—Dangerous
Should be Replaced

Don't
Forget
"Oliver"
First
Introduced
Safety
Cylinders
in
U. S. A.

Accident with "Oliver" Cylinder

Accident with Square Cutterhead

"Oliver" Circular Safety Cylinder

Approved

The laws of all states relative to safety appliances, and the requirements of liability insurance companies are so well observed when "Oliver" Safety Cylinders are used in Jointers, Scrapers, Moulders, etc., that factory inspectors and industrial boards heartily approve of the "Oliver" Safety Cylinders, as evidenced by the accompanying facsimile of the approval of the State of Pennsylvania.

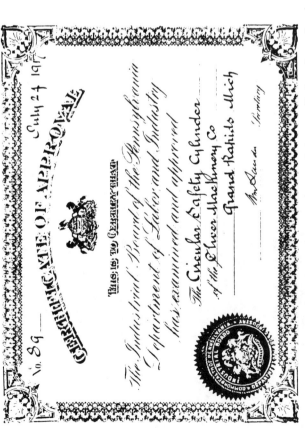

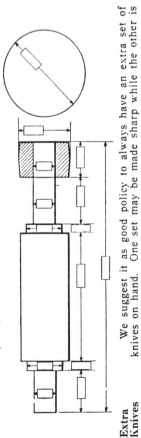

How to Order Cylinder

When desirous of installing one of these cylinders for a hand planer and jointer or a surface planer in use, it is necessary for us to have a drawing showing the actual dimensions of the old style cylinder, and the name of the maker of the machine.

Extra Knives

We suggest it as good policy to always have an extra set of knives on hand. One set may be made sharp while the other is in use.

Our Guarantee

Every Cylinder is guaranteed to be free from flaws, made correctly and perfectly satisfactory when properly operated. We have 6,500 of these cylinders in daily use.

Old Style—Dangerous

New Style "Oliver" Circular Safety Cylinder.

Oliver 1921 Catalog 21

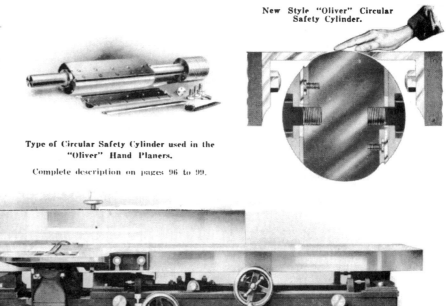

Type of Circular Safety Cylinder used in the "Oliver" Hand Planers.

Complete description on pages 96 to 99.

No. 12 "OLIVER" HAND PLANER AND JOINTER
Front View.

No. 12
"Oliver" Hand Planer and Jointer

Introduction This machine has been designed to meet the demands of a class of purchasers who recognize the fact that the best is cheapest. To produce it we have spared neither skilled labor nor material. They are used to plane smoothly, or true-up long or short pieces of lumber or timber, taking them out of wind, making glue joints, planing draft on pattern lumber, etc. Where high grade work is the requirement they are most profitable.

Bed This is very heavy, mounted on two cabinet columns, which places it on a very firm foundation, dissipating all vibration and allowing greatest foot room possible for the workman.

Tables Tables are rigid, proportionately made, and are provided with all the conveniences for promptly adjusting them to perform their functions. Front tables are 2" wider than the knives; rear tables are only 1" wider than the knives to allow rabbeting. The operating section is 2' longer than the front or stationary section. They rest on slides that are dovetailed into the bed and adjustable to and from the cut instantly.

Table Throats These tables are faced at the throat next the cutting cylinder with steel plates, which may be replaced at any time should the edges become badly nicked or worn from the use of special projecting knives or other causes.

Sliding Frames These carry the work tables and move in dovetailed ways planed in the bed. They are easily withdrawn for convenience in sharpening or removing knives. To them are bolted the shoes for the adjustment of the work tables, the rockers upon which the table rests, and also the screws and hand wheels which raise and lower for depth of cut.

Shoes These are tongued and grooved to the sliding frame and securely bolted. They also have large flat bearing surfaces and are gibbed by separate gibs running in slots which hold the work table securely to the sliding frame. These surfaces are all milled and accurately scraped and keep correct plane, or level, of the table at all times.

Cylinder Yoke This carries the cylinder and is made in one solid piece and bolted to the bed. This is a very desirable feature.

Cylinder We furnish with this machine Carston's Patent Circular Safety Cylinder which has all the advantages of the square cylinder and it saves hands. It is made of forged crucible steel and as regularly furnished carries two knives. It makes less noise than the old square cylinder, maintains a better balance, and uses all steel knives made from air hardening high speed steel,

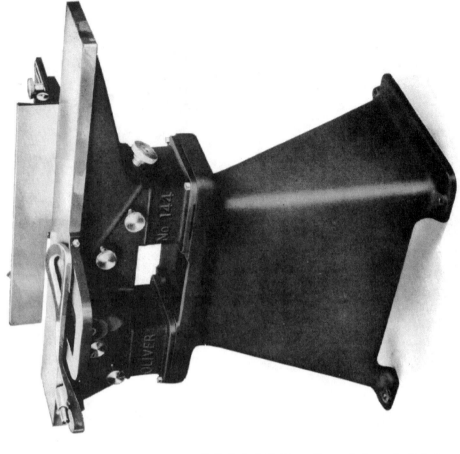

No. 144-B "OLIVER" BENCH HAND JOINTER ON CAST IRON COLUMN
With Rabbeting Arm Attachment.

No. 144

"Oliver" Hand Planer and Jointer

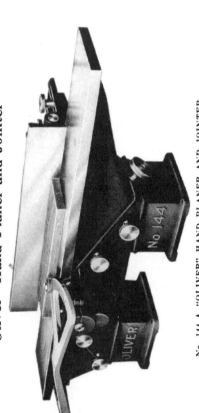

No. 144-A "OLIVER" HAND PLANER AND JOINTER
Showing Latest Style Aluminum Guard.

Introduction This machine is a quality producer in any workshop where hand planing is done either by the workman at his bench or by the other methods in vogue. While it has but a 6" head, it has the other features found on our heavy hand planers, performs every function, and can be relied upon for perfect planing. It is capable of doing a large percentage of the planing done by cabinet workers and others who ordinarily use the hand plane, and doing it better.

Frame This is in compact and rigid form, made of metal and may be bolted to a bench or mounted on a column (see special view).

Tables These are mounted on inclines and raised or lowered by means of hand wheel and screw. Both are dovetailed into the frame and may be locked firmly in any position.

Cylinder This is the celebrated "Oliver" Circular Safety type made of forged steel, carries two "Oliver" special Tungsten-Chromium thin knives and adjustable steel chip breakers. Insures safety to the operator and produces a higher grade of work. The pulley is the pneumatic type for increasing belt power.

Cylinder Bearings These are correct length, babbitted and scraped to proper fit. Wear can be taken up. They are self-oiling by wicks from oil reservoirs underneath.

Fence This is good length, very rigid and moves anywhere across the tables. It is easily held at any angle to 45 degrees.

Countershaft This is fitted with a steel ground shaft, two self-oiling hangers and the necessary pulleys. The loose pulley is bushed with bronze and is self-oiling.

107

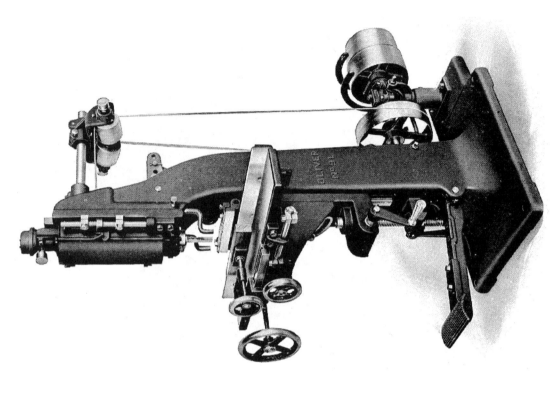

Oliver 1921 Catalog 21

No. 91 "OLIVER" VERTICAL HOLLOW CHISEL MORTISER. Machine also furnished with Motor Bracket for direct Motor Drive.

General View showing belt drive arrangement.

No. 91
"Oliver" Vertical Hollow Chisel Mortiser

Chisels and Bits quickly changed

Compound Tilting Table Regular

Introduction   This mortising machine performs its work by means of the hollow chisel, a form of tool now almost universally applied for all kinds of mortising operations. This chisel has a high speed bit revolving within it which serves both to bore a round hole and to remove the chips thus bored, as well as those cut out by the corners of the chisel. All chisels are accurately sized and thus mortise accurately, while operating smoothly, cleanly and without noise or vibration. They cut rapidly, due to the high bit speed possible with a supporting chisel, and are readily adapted to any shape of mortise, of any length or practical depth.

Column   The vertical type of mortiser is most popular and in this machine we offer a substantial, hollow vertical column with an extended base which offers support for either a self-contained countershaft or motor. This column carries the ways in which the spindle plunger operates and also those on which the table adjusts, correct alignment of the tools with the table being insured.

Plunger   The vertically reciprocating plunger carries the bit spindle with its drum driving pulley and also the chuck which holds the chisel. Its movement is controlled by foot lever, the length of stroke being adjustable according to the work. The return movement is accelerated by spring pressure. The foot lever is also adjustable in length and the belt pulley guarded. The spindle bearings are of guaranteed babbitt, self-lubricated from ample oil wells.

Table   The most satisfactory form of table for any hollow chisel machine is the compound type with a clamp and rack and pinion feed. While many pieces can be mortised without clamping there are others where clamping is necessary for straightening the stock or doing accurate work. Machines are sometimes cheapened by having plain tables, but such are deficient for general work.

No. 183 "OLIVER" HIGH SPEED DOUBLE SHAPER

Simple in Design; Powerful in Action; Durable in Operation; Second to None; Leader of Many

View showing application of No. 491 Shaper Guard, the new guards for spindle pulleys and regular equipment

No. 483
"Oliver" High Speed Double Spindle Shaper

Faster Work with Less Trouble

Introduction   The Wood Shaper or Variety Molder is one of the essential machines to a wood working plant. The style of work varies from rabbeting, grooving and fluting to shaping of every description. The illustrations represent our new High Speed Shaper, the machine that runs at extreme high speed without vibration.

Spindles   are large and tapering and are made of High Carbon Crucible Machinery Steel ground perfectly true on dead centers.

Bearings   are made of Bronze, conical in shape and are surrounded by oil chambers which lubricate the spindles the entire length of the bearings. The bottom of the spindle rides on a copper adjustable step which is constantly washed with oil. A large drip cup catches the waste oil from the upper bearings.

Pulleys   are carefully balanced and of the pneumatic type.

Yokes   are raised and lowered by means of the handwheels at the side of the machine, there being sufficient vertical adjustment to raise the spindle above the table or lower it beneath the tables. These yokes are very rigid and the screws for raising or lowering are directly in the rear of the spindle, affording them a direct support.

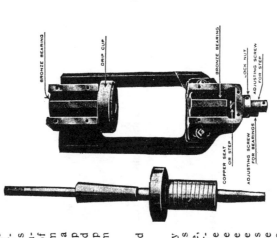

Showing Construction and Adjustment of High Speed Spindles and Bearings

Table   is large, very rigid, planed, and then accurately ground by a special process. It is bored out and fitted with three sets of rings to be used in connection with the knife collars.

Countershaft   furnished with each machine, consists of double adjustable hangers with ring oiling oiling boxes, drive pulleys, tight and loose pulleys (the loose pulley regularly furnished is bronze bushed, self-oiling and has a flange, but the Nelson patented loose pulley can be furnished on order at a slight additional cost), shaft collar and shifter. Two independent idlers or tighteners are also furnished with the machine. These idlers are well constructed, are adjustable and the bearings are bronze bushed and self-oiling, allowing separate adjustment for each belt.

109

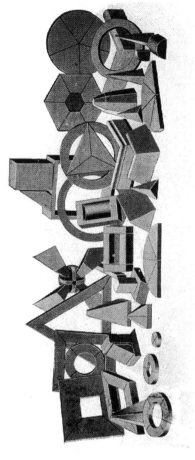

No. 41-B "OLIVER" DOUBLE DISK SANDER—37-inch
Note the Disk Guards and Dust Hoods Regularly Furnished

A few specimens of work that can be done on "Oliver" Disk Sanders

No. 41

"Oliver" Double Disk Sander 37-inch

Introduction — The economic value of sand paper is becoming more apparent every day and its application to the pattern makers' art is one of its most useful qualifications. The only difference between grinding iron and wood on a disk sander is that you can grind wood many times faster. Five minutes of sanding on a piece of wood will frequently accomplish more than an hour would any other way. It smooths up end grain and puts draft on it. It sands out saw marks. In repairing patterns the broken piece that is usually thrown away because it is full of brads or nails, may be sanded nails and all and saved.

A large disk is more desirable than a small one because the sand paper farthest from the center does the most work.

General Construction — This very desirable sander is constructed from a new design and has embodied in the design and superior workmanship that which renders it subject to the most searching inspection. If one has important and variable sanding to do he should not ignore this very efficient source of economy.

Base — We build this in the cored form with a wide flange for rigid support on the floor. It carries all the working parts and its solidity eliminates vibration. On the front is a door through which may be introduced a motor for electric drive.

Spindle — This is of fine crucible steel, ground true and fitted at each end to receive the metal disks. Its driving pulley is grooved spirally on its face to permit increase of belt power.

Bearings — They are lined with guaranteed babbitt scraped to correct fit, have large oil chambers and wick oilers. End motion to spindle is eliminated by means of forged collar on the spindle between disk and bearings and adjustable keyed and set screwed pulley against babbitt thrust bearing.

Disks — These are of steel 37½" diameter machined to receive the sand paper and are screwed to the spindle by four large countersunk screws. The paper is cemented to face of disk.

Dust Hoods — A sheet steel dust exhaust hood for each disk is located just below the table top with a connecting spout to each hood. Prevents dust from being scattered about the room.

Disk Guards — Sheet steel guards to protect operator against danger from that part of disks above the table are furnished regularly with each machine.

110

No. 34 "OLIVER" VERTICAL SPINDLE AND DISK SANDER
Made in two sizes, 24-inch and 30-inch diameter disks.
Front View showing method of tilting table.

No. 34
"Oliver" Vertical Spindle and Disk Sander

Ball Bearings and Single Belt Drive
24-inch and 30-inch Disk

Introduction   In this machine are incorporated all of the best features found in any disk and spindle sander. The driving is all done through a single spindle. The disk shaft is connected to the drum by means of a standard friction transmission. The machine is ball bearing throughout with double row thrust bearings for each spindle, full enclosed and protected.

Economy   By the use of highest quality ball bearings and the simple transmission, the machine requires practically no more power applied to the belt than is used at the point of sanding.

Main Frame   Is heavy, made of one casting in the cored form with large flanged base measuring 28" x 28" at the floor.

Disk Table   Is machined true with grooves to receive centering plates, duplicating attachment and angle gauge. The disk table is counterbalanced by weights operating inside the column. There is a positive clamping device for holding table in position on column. Disk table tilts 10 degrees up and 45 degrees down. The disk table moves back 4" from the disk. Table is adjustable both above and below the center of the disk. The tilting mechanism forms the bracket on which the table rests. The heavy cast iron machined rockers are so arranged that the pivoted center is exactly in the plane of the disk.

Spindle Table   Is 26" x 30", height from floor 42". Table tilts 45 degrees forward and 5 degrees backward. Provided with removable metal throat pieces closely fitting the 2", 3" or 4" drums respectively.

Disk   This is 24" or 30" in diameter, made of steel ½" thick, machined in such a way that the paper easily adheres to it and tested for running balance. The center of the disk is 32" from the floor. Hood is so arranged as to connect conveniently with an exhaust pipe.

Can operate disk without running spindle. The latter can be instantly thrown into or out of operation by simply moving one lever, which is conveniently placed.

Vertical Spindle   The vertical spindle is 1⅜" diameter, fitted with high grade ball bearings. The oscillating mechanism is operated from spindle through worm and gear in oil, making fifty strokes per minute. The oscillating travel of drum is 1⅛". Standard length of drums 9".

111

No. 24
"Oliver" Double End Wood Lathe

No. 24 "OLIVER" PATTERN MAKER'S WOOD LATHE
16, 20, 24, and 30 inch Swing with Hand Feeding Carriage and Compound Swivel Rest.

Modern shop practice in wood turning demands a higher type of lathe than formerly. Alive to this situation we have met the demand in the No. 24 Lathe described herein.

Head Stock It is made from a cored casting of the proper strength and rigidity, and well proportioned. It may be swiveled for taper turning, about 5 degrees each way from the center.

Head Spindle We make it of fine crucible steel, large in diameter and threaded at both ends to receive face plates. It is made with hole through it to assist in securing work to face plates. It is accurately ground and is absolutely true in the journals.

Spindle Bearings and Cone These are lined with guaranteed babbitt, are adjustable to wear, and are fitted with oil chambers for self-lubrication. The spindle cone is made of cast iron, has four steps, machined all over and adjusted to a running balance.

End Thrust It is taken care of by means of thrust collars threaded to the spindle. A loose bronze collar bears against each end of the rear journal box and plays between the solid collar on the spindle on one end and the thrust collars on the other.

Tail Stock It is constructed in the open side design. Cutting tools may be brought close to centers. It has set-over device for turning taper work, and an eccentric lever for locking it any desired position. The tail spindle is of correct diameter bored to Morse tapers. It is held in position by means of a strong clamp. The tail center may be removed by simply backing the screw.

Arranged with 8 and 10 foot long metal beds. Power Feeding Carriage and Compound Swivel Rest. Made in four sizes, to swing over the bed 16, 20, 24, and 30 inch diameter.

The Bed It is of iron of proportionate dimensions to suit the size of the lathe. It can be supplied in any length, six feet or more, calculating by advances of two feet. It has a broad top, made flat so the operator's tools will not work off. When furnished to receive a tool carriage the ways for same are cast to the side.

Power Feeding Carriage The call for this machine fitted with a carriage that is fed automatically as well as by hand has resulted in the design of carriage shown in the accompanying half-tone. All sizes of lathes are recommended and regularly provided with it. However, when hand-feeding carriage only is especially desired, same is furnished at a slight difference in price. The carriage receives its power through a belt from a two-step cone on the lathe spindle to a cone on the feed shaft, giving two speeds to the feed shaft. When using the lathe at the overhanging end for face turning on large diameters the cone pulley may be instantly removed.

Compound Swivel Rest We locate a graduated swivel device on the cross slide of the tool carriage, which permits the use of the tool on angular lines. By means of the graduations the tool may be set with great exactness. It has a long traverse and any conceivable angle may be correctly obtained.

No. 19 "OLIVER" IMPROVED SPEED LATHE—12-inch.
View showing Hand Feeding Carriage, Compound Swivel Rest, Set-over Tail Stock and arrangement for Rear End Turning, including an 8-inch Rear End Face Plate, all of which are extras furnished only when so ordered.

No. 19-A PLAIN BED SPEED LATHE
Rear View

No. 19-A PLAIN BED SPEED LATHE
Front View

Oliver 1921 Catalog 21

No. 19
"Oliver" Improved Speed Lathe 12-inch

Introduction This demand for a Speed Lathe that is well designed, correctly built, substantial, powerful and easily operated, has been met by the No. 19 Machine here illustrated. We make no claims for "cheapness" in the ordinary acceptance of the word.

Head Stock This is made in the cored form, and has a clean cut design. The base is fitted to the bed and securely bolted by bar clamps.

Head Spindle It is of crucible steel, machine ground, made hollow and the front end threaded to receive face plates, hollow chucks, screw chucks, etc. Center hole fitted for No. 2 Morse Taper.

Bearings These are supplied with split bronze bushings grooved inside for oil passage, and fitted with brass ring oiling device. A constant film of oil covers the journals with no danger of scattering it. Wear of spindle is compensated for by adjustable caps.

Spindle Cone This is of metal finished to a running balance, has four steps very ingeniously designed so that the smallest step can be screwed out to take up all end motion; the larger three steps are keyed to the spindle so that the entire cone pulley is rigidly held and can never cause any trouble. The cone pulley may be locked by means of a hook, while face plates are screwed on or off.

End Thrust This is cared for by the ends of the cone pulley pressing against the bronze bushings. Adjustment is made by expanding the cone. The smallest step being threaded into the balance of the cone.

Tail Stock This is open side design, permits cutting tools to reach the centers and provides a pocket for holding small tools. A hand lever with a shaped concave end piece clamps the spindle and a hand lever clamps the tail stock at any position on the bed.

Tail Spindle We make this correct diameter and bore it for No. 2 Morse taper. The end of the hand wheel rod, which is fastened by screwing a sleeve into the tail stock casting, is square threaded into the tail spindle and operates easily. The tail center may be removed by backing up the screw.

Bed This is of metal, well ribbed and free from vibration. The broad top of the bed is flat and will receive the operator's tools without danger of their working off and becoming lost. Two metal brackets on the back to receive a tool board are provided. It is made to stand on the floor or be placed on a bench as desired.

113

No. 20 MOTOR DRIVE PATTERN MAKER'S WOOD LATHE

No. 20
"Oliver" Motor Drive Pattern Maker's Wood Lathe

Arranged for Using Alternating Current Motor

Introduction — To successfully meet the demand for a self-contained lathe that can be driven by an A. C. motor, we have furnished the machine as shown and described herewith. We recommend it as capable of proving absolutely satisfactory.

Motor — We recommend alternating current, two speed, 600, 1200 R. P. M. motor. giving 8 speeds to spindle. Motor is supported under the lathe bed and fitted with a four step cone pulley accurately balanced. A vertical adjustment serves to keep the belt tight. A self-oiling bearing carries the outer end of the armature shaft with cone pulley.

Head Stock — This is similar to the one on the No. 24 Lathe. The base is widened to permit the driving belt to pass through to the cone on the motor shaft. Head spindle is fine steel, machine ground, and cone is metal fitted to a running balance.

Tail Stock — It is open side design with large steel spindle bored to Morse Taper. It is supported rigidly in all its positions.

Bed — This is similar to the metal beds supplied with the No. 24 Lathe. The end that receives the head stock is widened to permit the belt to pass through.

Power Feeding Carriage — The carriage is regularly fitted with a compound swivel rest having ample lateral movement, wide bearing on the ways. It receives its power through a belt from a two-step cone on the lathe spindle to a cone on a feed shaft placed the length of the bed, giving two speeds to the feed shaft.

Equipment — Power or hand feeding carriage and compound swivel rest; two spur centers, one cup center, one pair conical centers, three face plates, each 8", 14", and 20" diameter; one screw chuck. 3½"; two single shank rests, 6" and 18" long; one double shank rest, 30" long; two rest holders with clamps, one rest holder fitted to tool post on carriage, one right angle rest 6" long, one portable floor stand with off-set rest holder. For exact equipment with each size, see table of equipment on page 141.

No.	Size	Swing Over Bed	Swing at Carriage	Swing at Outer end Head Spindle	Turns Between Centers	Standard Length Bed	Dom. Weight	For. Weight	Cu. Ft.
20-A	16"	16"	13"	84"	5'	8'	2250	2500	104
20-B	20"	20"	17"	84"	4' 6"	8'	2800	3100	133
20-C	24"	24"	20"	84"	6'	10'	3800	4200	136
20-D	30"	30"	26"	84"	5' 6"	10'	4600	5000	144

THE OLIVER MACHINERY COMPANY

No. 74
"Oliver" Universal Vertical and Horizontal Borer

Ball Bearings—Two Spindle

No. 74-A "OLIVER" UNIVERSAL VERTICAL AND HORIZONTAL BORER

Introduction   We have designed this with the idea of supplying to the trade a heavier and more desirable machine for boring purposes than is usually offered. Those who find ordinary boring machines too light and weak for their purpose are particularly requested to study this Borer.

Adaptation   This is an extraordinary borer—it will not only respond with satisfaction to all kinds of boring machine work, but will also drill holes in iron or do the work of a router, shaper, buzz planer or sandpaper machine. A little safety cylinder, similar to that used on our No. 144 jointer, applied to this machine opens up an endless variety of work that this machine will easily take care of. A variety of sanding spindle helps to smooth up many otherwise almost inaccessible places.

The machine is built right, works right and we can recommend it as an "Oliver Tool."

No. 74-B "OLIVER" MOTOR DRIVEN UNIVERSAL VERTICAL AND HORIZONTAL BORER

Capacity   Vertical spindle will bore 12" deep to center of 36". Horizontal spindle will bore 7" deep. Both spindles will readily bore holes 3" diameter and under.

Oliver 1921 Catalog 21

Oliver 1921 Catalog 21

No. 75
"Oliver" Wood Milling Machine

Adaptation — For the general pattern shop where good work is appreciated. It does the most difficult work very simply and very easily. This machine is to the pattern shop what the milling machine is to the tool room. The same dividing head may be used not only for cutting gear teeth, but also for dividing off and machining duplicate work on similar segments or sections of the same piece. It is a machine that improves with acquaintance, although the operator quickly grasps the idea and general working of the machine, it is a matter of time for him to realize to the fullest extent the operations it can perform, since it is only as extraordinary shapes are brought to him that he gradually sees that the flexibility of the machine renders its range of operations practically unlimited. Hours you spent then now mean **minutes** on this machine on any of the following operations:

Kind of Work — Core Boxes, regular and irregular, any section.
Square Bends, S Bends, Tees, Socket Ends, Valve Boxes, etc.
Regular and Irregular Patterns to match the above.
Cross Grooving, Trenching, Halving, Jointing, Cross Cutting.
Recessing, Routing, cut heavy bodies, Rounding Curves.
Shaping U D and C Shaped Sections.
Truing up Sectional Built-up Pieces direct from the saw.
Boring and Slotting large size holes at any angle.
Facing, Cutting Port Holes.
Shaping straight or curved Arms of Wheels, and bases of same.
Recessing and trenching of every description and variety.
Gear Cutting.
Boring up to 6 inches or larger by rotating the work table.
Cutting Fillets, straight or curved.
Cutting Dowels crosswise of the grain.
Straight Corner Locking Half Lapping Jointing, Ploughing.
Slot Mortising and Recessing any length up to 6" wide.
Shaping Square to any design, size or length.
Tenoning, double or single, and scribing at one operation.
Dovetailing right and left hand sets at one setting.

Tools Needed — Most of the above operations may be accomplished with the tools provided with the machine and others can be quickly made to suit special work.

Bearings — Both vertical and horizontal spindles run on ball bearings of large diameter, allowing a maximum speed of 5000 R. P. M., if desirable, on certain work. Regular speeds of each spindle on No. 75-A and B are 1250, 2000, 3000 and 4300 R. P. M. Idler pulleys are 10" diameter and 4" face, and are provided with ball bearings, thus eliminating all lubrication troubles of high speed loose pulleys. The countershaft bearings are of genuine babbitt, as the slower speeds render ball bearings needless, and the loose driving pulley is bushed with self-oiling bronze bushing.

Column — Cored type with ample flange support bolted to base. Vertical ways 10¾" wide across face, extending far enough to give perfect bearing to knee in either highest or lowest position. Height over all, 7′ 0″.

Base — Or sole plate 28″x60″ planed to receive column and telescoping screw bracket. On No. 75-B this plate is extended to receive motor.

No. 75-A WOOD MILLING MACHINE—Front View Belt Drive

Chapter 5

BUYING VINTAGE WOODWORKING MACHINERY

ESTABLISHING THE VALUE

"What's it worth?" is a basic question asked by someone who has acquired a piece of old woodworking machinery or who is thinking of buying. So perhaps a few pointers and guidelines would be helpful.

The art of pricing woodworking machinery, like all skills, comes with experience. There are too many variables–what kind of bearings (babbitt bearing machines are worth less), drive (flat belt driven machines are worth less), size, condition, etc.–to permit a definitive answer. How bad do you want it? How bad does the seller need money? Who is the manufacturer? How rare is the machine? Even geography can influence price.

Clearly, the average person needs a quick, general guideline to evaluate machines and come up with some sort of a working price. As a modest collector of trade catalogs dealing with woodworking machinery, and a buyer and user of such equipment, it is my opinion that, condition aside, the weight of a machine is the most accurate reflection of its quality. Heavier is better. Therefore I have arrived at a mathematical formula, described below, that I often use myself to assign a value, albeit arbitrary, for negotiating a price.

Woodworking machines are almost always made of cast iron. I tend to stay away from aluminum (which became popular after the Second World War because of a surplus) and from welded steel; I consider both materials inferior. They are fine for the average hobbyist but a disappointment to the serious craftsman.

A few words on condition. I define poor condition as having broken or missing major parts (such as a jointer fence), badly rusted surfaces, clearly visible cracks in cast iron structural parts or working surfaces, bad bearings (babbitt bearings are harder to replace), or badly worn parts (such as gears and lifting screws). A machine in poor condition probably requires a complete restoration, including purchasing or fabricating new parts, and this is not a cheap proposition.

Good condition means that no important parts are broken or missing (knobs and handles are easily replaced) and that the bearings are sound; it permits, for example, a few minor cracks in the cast iron, some slightly worn parts (many production quality machines have built-in adjustments to compensate for wear), and light rust. Basically, all that is needed is a good cleaning and some minor repairs and adjustments.

Excellent condition means that the machine looks new, has seen little use, and for, all practical purposes, is ready to run.

Pricing the machine, for me, is fairly straightforward. For a machine in good condition, I estimate its weight (excluding motor) and multiply the number of pounds by 65¢. Naturally, accessories would increase the price. A machine in poor condition is worth only local scrap metal price. A machine in excellent condition is worth about $1 a pound. I must emphasize that these are guidelines only, as other factors can influence price.

This formula works very well up to a point. As you get into the truly monstrous production machinery, the market rapidly gets smaller. While an ambitious hobbyist may be willing to add a 1900 pound Yates-American Model 199 12" jointer to his shop, very few people need or want a 15,000 pound Yates-American 30" x 6" Model 95 Planer and Matcher!

Woodworking machinery is a different kind of antique animal. Don't let age inflate the price. Few people buy machinery to look at; most put it back into operation. Ten years old or one hundred years old, it doesn't matter much to a woodworker. Very few of us will pay a premium for age. Quality of manufacture and condition are the important factors.

ESTABLISHING THE AGE

The first step in the restoration process is to determine the age of the machine. Many craftsmen consider the years between 1920 and 1960 the golden age of woodworking machinery and restrict themselves to those years. Machines of that period were still solidly built, ball bearings were becoming the rule, square cutter heads were on the way out, and electric motors were coming in. Others, like myself, prefer pre-1920 machines, enjoying the nostalgia as much as the machine.

Sometimes one gets just plain curious about the age of a machine picked up at a flea market or auction. Seldom does a machine bear a date of manufacture. However, there are several clues that can be strung together to yield a general idea.

If you're fortunate enough to have some sort of paper documentation associated with the machine—shipping label, sales sticker, manual, etc.—you can generally work out an approximate date. For example, postal zones were added to business addresses after 1943. the five number zip code dates from 1963 and the nine number code was added in 1976. A telephone number with fewer than seven digits dates from 1896 to 1945.

Usually a machine will carry a patent number. This can date a machine to within a few decades. Patent number 1 was issued in 1836. Patent numbers 1 through 550,000 run to 1895 and 550,001 through 2,300,000 to 1945. Patent numbers were nearing 4,000,000 in 1976 and now exceed 4,600,000.

Machine construction itself can be of help. However, remember that woodworkers, like other craftsmen, are continually modifying equipment. Retro-fitting is hardly a new concept. Many of us don't follow the maxim "If it ain't broke, don't fix it." For example, flat belts were replaced by V-belts, square cutterheads with round heads.

A square cutterhead could indicate pre-1908 construction. The patent for the round safety head in the United States dates from January 1908. Keep in mind, however, that many companies not only supplied replacement round heads, but continued to furnish square heads, if preferred, well into the 1930s.

Ball bearings were available as early as 1908, usually as a special order for jointers. By 1923, they were available as regular features on most machines. Between 1920 and 1930, nearly all woodworking machinery was redesigned for direct motor drives and ball bearings.

In 1909 thin, high-speed knives (mounted in circular heads) started to appear in jointers, planers, moulders, etc. The rubber V-belt made its appearance around 1930. A machine with flat belt pulleys would be early 1800 - late 1920 vintage.

By 1906 direct-current (DC) motors running 720-1000 rpms were being operated, fastened directly to machine countershafts. The alternating current (AC) motor came into use circa 1919. These first motors were mounted directly on cutterhead arbors still running in Babbitt bearings. Machines with cutter spindles mounted on ball bearings and driven by direct drive motors date from 1920-1930.

About 1923 the first light-duty homeshop woodworking machines began to be manufactured, most designed to plug directly into a light socket.

OBTAINING PARTS

You've knowingly bought a piece of woodworking machinery with damaged or lost parts, or discovered it afterwards much to your chagrin? You want an owner's manual, or need replacement parts, or you're just plain curious about the firm that made it? But where do you go for help? Availability of parts is a troubling part of machine restoration.

The first step is to start at the beginning and determine whether or not the company still exists.

You can determine this quickly by consulting the *Thomas Register of American Manufacturers,* one of the most comprehensive directories of U.S. manufacturers now in print. The documentation includes a list of manufacturers classified by product and arranged geographically, with ratings of their capital; an alphabetical list of manufacturers, with their home and branch offices, subsidiaries, cable addresses, phone and fax numbers; and an alphabetical list of company trade names.

The very similar *McRae's Blue Book,* an annual directory of American industry, can provide additional company background information and, like the *Thomas Register,* occasionally carries illustrated ads featuring machinery. Both also list companies that recondition machines and custom fabricate parts.

If the company is still in business, you're in good shape. If not, then more trips to the library are in your future.

When you communicate with an still-existent machinery manufacturer, give them full details on the machine—type, model number, serial number, patent number, size, etc. You may have to go over every inch of the machine for a number and finally end up poking your head and a flashlight into its insides, and still find none. Finally, always include a self-addressed, stamped envelope for their response.

This is as good a place as any to discuss etiquette. The representatives you'll deal with are busy men and women. Even if they want to help, their regular duties make it difficult to give much time to your requests. Be specific and clear in your questions and keep them few.

However, don't be surprised if the company doesn't offer any assistance. Yates-American absolutely refuses to service its vintage machines and urges that they immediately be removed from service. One of the worst problems being faced by older companies are lawsuits. One story has become legendary. A few years ago, a careless woodworker cut his hand off using a 100+ year old bandsaw. Though the bandsaw met all the required standards of the time, the plaintiff's attorney convinced a jury that the company was still liable.

The president of one of California's oldest woodworking machinery manufacturers came up with a novel way to deal with the problem. He used to visit auctions with the intention of buying back any of the company's old planers going at bargain prices. It was one less machine it had to worry about. Before its demise a few years ago, the company had a room full of such machines.

Until Congress finishes revising a long-standing bill dealing with outdated liability laws, manufacturers will be leery of giving help.

Obtaining more information will take time, patience, work, and some money. Local sources will be the best help here. Contact the library located in the manufacturer's home town. The *American Library Directory* lists public libraries; state and regional library systems; junior college, college, and university libraries; special libraries; private libraries; and government libraries. The arrangement is by state and city, covering the U.S. and its territories, and Canada. Data given includes special departments and collections. If this volume is unobtainable, a letter will usually get to the local library by simply addressing it: The (City) Public Library, (City), (State) (Zip). Don't overlook state, specialized, and university libraries near the manufacturer.

Sad to say, many local and state historical societies have nothing or next to nothing on manufacturers in their areas–even large, old firms, employing hundreds, that had been operating until recent times. The New England states and communities, however, seem to have done much more along these lines. *The Directory of Historical Societies and Agencies in the United States and Canada* lists national, state, and provincial historical organizations of all types, as does the *Historical Societies in the United States and Canada: A Handbook.* The latter is arranged by state and lists state and local historical historical societies, giving a brief description of their history and activities.

The Patent and Trademark Office of the United States Dept. of Commerce (Commissioner of Patents and Trademarks, Washington DC 20231) can occasionally be helpful. Printed copies of any patent, identified by its patent number, may be purchased from the office for a nominal fee. A current fee schedule is available.

However, if there is no patent number on the machine, you've hit a snag. A search of Patent and Trademark Office records can only be made if the following information is provided:

- The name of the inventor (the Office doesn't make searches by a manufacturer or by any other assignee of the patent rights).

- The approximate date of the invention, or the years you wish searched.

- The title or the subject matter of the invention.

The fee, paid in advance, for searching the records is $10 per half hour or fraction thereof. A 10-year period can usually be done in that amount of time.

A final source of possible information is museums. The *Handbook of American Museums* provides a list of about 1,400 museums of all types, arranged geographically by city and state. It gives basic information about each one's history, collections, and publications. Even though it may be out-of-date, much of the information is still accurate–museums tend to stay put. A Canadian list is appended.

In addition, the author, in order to raise needed research funds to prepare future volumes, sells selected photocopies from his growing collection of old catalogs, manuals, and parts lists.

RESTORING A FAY & EGAN JOINTER: A CASE STUDY

The biggest restoration project I ever undertook was getting a circa 1912 J.A. Fay & Egan Co. Model 61 16-inch jointer up and running; it can serve as an example of how to go about the task.

Purchased for $250 several years ago, this machine had the following defects: the aluminum guard had been broken and bolted back together; two 7/8 x 16 bolts in the two-knife round cutterhead were missing; several holes in the cutterhead had defaced threads; the tables, fence, and adjusting wheels were badly rusted; the tables were misaligned; and a flat belt was needed. I also decided to preserve the original knives bearing Fay & Egan's name and replace them with two new ones.

I soon discovered that the best help for locating special services and supplies and off-the-shelf hardware came from the local yellow pages and regional industrial buying guides, such as those issued annually by the Thomas Regional Directory Co.

Though guards (such as those on jointers) can usually be fabricated out of wood, I located a nearby welder in the phone book and had the broken guard re-welded for $12.

I also got lucky on the missing cutterhead bolts. My old high school shop teacher, when he learned of my problem, volunteered to make new ones on his metal lathe. A machine shop would have done the same job.

After making several calls to local machine shops and friends, I decided to order a new tap to recut the threads in the cutterhead. I found that J & L Industrial Supply Co. of Detroit and Chicago not only regularly carries standard and obsolete taps and dies in a wide range of variations, including carbide, but would also make custom ones. The price was very reasonable and delivery was quick.

The McMaster-Carr Supply Co. of Los Angeles also carries a wide range of industrial supplies and hardware, including power transmission equipment (belts, pulleys, Babbitting supplies, etc.).

The tables and fence were cleaned by going over them with a quarter sheet palm sander beginning with 240 grit, followed by 320 and 400. This was followed by 0000 steel wool, rubbing compound, and a coat of paste wax.

Stubborn nuts, bolts, pulleys, etc., were freed using a penetrating lubricant called Ferro-Slick, which can be bought at welding suppliers. After a brief soak, they readily came apart with a wrench or socket after a few taps with a deadblow hammer.

As a point of interest, I accidentally discovered the original color of my jointer (black) by looking at the underside of the fence. Other protected surfaces can guide you in matching colors. Almost any paint department can now computer-match and mix the the color.

A new 3-foot flat belt was purchased at a local power transmission shop. The firm also carried a vast array of ball and roller bearings. All such firms have people who are expert at identifying and matching bearings and who are very helpful in giving directions on how to remove and install bearings.

My machine had babbitt bearings which were still sound, saving much time. But the materials for repouring your own, and the directions for doing so, can still be found. The very best guide on how to do it, "Repouring Babbitt Bearings, A Low-Tech Way to Rescue Old Machines," by Bob Johnson, appears in *Woodworking Machines* published by Taunton Press. Before use, I always give my jointer's bearings a generous squirt of new heavy-duty motor oil.

New knives were purchased from Charles G.G. Schmidt & Co. of Montvale, NJ. Schmidt carries a wide range of standard and custom-ground knives for jointers, shapers, moulders, etc., even slotted planer knives. Carbide is usually an option as well.

If you need bandsaw wheels recovered, cemented, ground, and/or balanced, Woodworkers' Tool Works of Black River Falls, WI, can do the job. Tires and cement are also available for the do-it-yourselfer.

I've found that the people representing such companies really do want to satisfy and can often give advice on how to determine what you need. If they don't have it, some will even suggest a competitor who might have what you need.

By accident I discovered that most of the the directions for calibrating Oliver Machinery Co.'s No. 12 Hand Planer and Jointer were applicable to the Fay & Egan jointer. So it's smart to study any manuals you can get your hands on.

A final tip on safety. Before running any old machine I've "restored," I operate it by hand first. Turn the driving pulley to make sure there is clearance and no wobble. When you put it under power, stand well clear.

Finally, never buy a square-headed jointer with the intention of actually using it. I can guarantee you'll lose several fingers. These jointers are accidents looking for a place to happen. Keep them as examples of early woodworking machinery only. However, I have owned and operated a 24 x 8 inch Defiance Machine Co. square-headed planer for several years with no problems.

Chapter 6

RESTORING WOODWORKING MACHINERY

In 1978 when I first started my custom woodworking business in the living room of my home in New Mexico, I had no knowledge of vintage woodworking machinery. I equipped my shop on a shoestring with a cheap Sears bandsaw and tablesaw. The tablesaw was continually overloading and shutting off, and the bandsaw spun a bearing and ate a shaft, requiring me to introduce myself to the local machinist. In 1980 I moved back to New Jersey, and my shop started to grow. As it grew, my requirements for quality machinery grew with it. Since New Jersey was, in its heyday, a large manufacturing area, there was an abundance of used woodworking machinery available. I visited Rudolph Bass (a large machinery dealer) to look at new machines, but I became intrigued by the aisles and aisles of classic old machines that were for sale there. Once I started using some of this industrial equipment, I was hooked. No longer could I go back to my former machines. From then on it seemed that I didn't have to go looking for machinery; it would find me.

The buyer of vintage woodworking machinery is either a user or a collecter. The collector is usually more interested in the physical appearance, both aesthetically and mechanically, and/or the historical significance. The user, by definition, is looking for a machine that can do the job. Since most modern industrial equipment is priced out of the average woodworker's budget, more and more people are finding that vintage machinery is, in many cases, far superior to new machines and costs far less money. For example, a vintage patternmaker's lathe that would cost $20,000 new

could be bought from a used machinery dealer for $7000 - $10,000, at an auction for about $3000, and, if you got lucky, from a private individual for $500 - $2000. And that lathe, properly restored, would undoubtedly be of better quality than most new machinery. This is not to say that all used machinery is quality machinery, or that all used machinery is cost effective to restore. I've thrown a lot of time and money into machines that I never got to run right—but that is part of the learning process.

BUYING VINTAGE MACHINERY

Where to look

There are many ways to go about finding old machines. Certainly, if you live in or around an established manufacturing area, your chances are greatly improved, but machinery is also available in the most unlikely places.

The first thing to do is to network — let everyone know you are interested in old machinery and follow up on any leads. You'll be amazed at the phone calls you will get right out of the blue.

There are many used machinery dealers around: check the yellow pages, ask your lumber yard, or look in the trade magazines. Woodworking magazines like *Fine Woodworking* feature classified ads. *Woodshop News* has a large machinery classified section, plus ads from dealers. I've also had good luck in the local want-ad press, as well as in newspaper classifieds.

Antique shows and antique tool auctions are also possibilities, though you will probably find smaller and more expensive machines, geared towards the collector, e.g., treadle machines, watchmaker's lathes, and the like. Even garage sales and flea markets can turn up some interesting items. Auctions are great too, especially wood shop and pattern shop liquidations. Machinery dealers may also be at these auctions, but they are generally more interested in big ticket items and usually drop out while the bidding is still in the "good deal" range. Be sure to leave time to examine the equipment thoroughly before it goes on the block – many bad deals are made in the heat of bidding.

Make friends with the people at your local scrap metal yard; they will sell you machinery they get at scrap metal prices, if they haven't already cut it up. School wood shops, military installations, and boat yards are also good bets for quality machinery. And if you hear of a pattern shop that is going out of business, check it out, because no one uses finer equipment, or keeps it in better condition, than patternmakers.

What to bring

It's okay just to look over a piece of machinery before buying if you're a collector, but if you're serious about using it, you'd be well advised to bring some tools with you. The first tool you need to bring is a good flashlight. A machine can look a lot better in some dim corner of a woodshop than it does when you get it home, under bright lights. It's also a good idea to examine the insides of the machine with your light.

A dial indicator with a flexible neck and magnetic base is also a must for your tool kit. I'll describe later how it is used to determine run-out, end play, concentricity, and parallel. A long, accurate, straight edge is also a must, preferably four feet long, minimum three. This will be used to check tables, fences, platens, etc., for straightness.

A square is necessary to check parts that are meant to be at right angles, such as fences and spindles. Wrenches and screwdrivers are also useful for inspecting machinery, for example opening cover plates, oil fill plugs, cutter guards, etc. A set of winding sticks is useful to check if joiner and planer tables are in the same plane. Don't just accept that the condition of a machine is what the seller tells you it is; check it out for yourself.

What to look for

Usually when you examine a machine for the first time, you are assessing its quality and condition. Quality, as I mentioned before, is a function of how well the machine was made and how many of the original accessories are still with it. Generally speaking, the best useable American machines were made between 1910 and 1950. However, there were also a lot of mediocre machines made during that period that are not worth the time and money to restore. Quality early twentieth century American manufacturers include Oliver, Yates-American, Fay & Egan, Tannewitz, Whitney, Moak, Defiance, American, Wallace, Beach, Walker Turner, and Root, to name a few. Some of the more recent quality names are early Sears, Roebuck, Rockwell, Ekstrom-Carlson, DeWalt, and Powermatic.

After you have determined the quality of the machine, it is important to take a close look at its condition. Don't let your excitement at finding a classic machine cloud your judgment of its condition. Over the years, machines used in industrial shops get a lot of use, and often abuse. Here are some important things to look for:

Modifications

Many machines have been modified during the course of their lives. Sometimes the modifications can be good. Babbitt bearings were often replaced with bolt-on bearing blocks containing ball bearings. Square cutterheads were replaced with round. Remote-powered flat-belt-driven systems were replaced with motors and V-belts, and guards were fabricated and installed where there were none.

However, not all modifications are worthwhile or well done. Some machines have been modified to suit a specific operation and are no longer useful for their original purpose. Modifications are usually quite easy to spot, but you must look carefully and assume nothing.

Cracks in Castings

Nothing will ruin your day more quickly than getting a machine home only to find that a major casting is cracked. Cast iron can be welded, but it's not easy and the heat used in the process can distort the casting or cause cracks elsewhere. Another way to treat minor cracks in cast iron is to stop them from spreading by simply drilling a hole at the end. Generally, cracks in non-essential areas such as motor mounts, table bases, and guards are not necessarily critical. However, cracked tables, spindle housings, lathe ways, etc., can mean doom for a successful restoration. Look closely with a good light; cast iron is brittle and many castings are cracked.

Missing Parts

Most old machines have at least some missing parts. If they are generic, like cutters, bolts, knobs, etc., it will probably not be a problem, but if they are major, like fences, drive gears, tool posts, etc., it may be a very expensive proposition to get your machine operational. If the manufacturer is still around, it may be possible to order these parts, although you may be floored by the price. Otherwise, you will have to try to find these parts at used machinery dealers, or have them fabricated, which can also be incredibly expensive.

Phase of the Motor

Motors are usually not a problem with used machinery, although they occasionally burn out or need replacement bearings. What is important is to check the phase of the motor. Most industrial woodworking machinery is 3-phase. This means that it will not work off a standard household 110/120 volt outlet. If it's a belt-driven, 3-phase motor and you don't have 3-phase power, you can replace the motor with a single phase motor which, if you buy it new, will run around $100 per horsepower. You may also need to modify the mount and change the pulleys. However, if it's direct drive 3-phase, you won't be able to use it unless you buy a phase converter. These can cost several hundred dollars. If the windings on the motor are burned out, it can be re-wound at your local motor repair shop, but expect to spend a few hundred dollars, depending on the motor.

Condition of Tables

The cast iron tables on old machinery may have seen a lot of use over the years; often they have been used so much that deep grooves and gullies have been worn into them. Often, tables have warped and twisted. Something heavy may have been dropped on them, or the machine may have fallen over. On some machines, a table that is not flat is not as critical as on others. Joiners, planers, molders, and boring machines depend on flat tables for accuracy. On machines like jig saws, table saws, band saws, and stroke sanders, this is not as critical. A slightly warped table can be machined flat, but again, this can be costly, as well as resulting in a thinner table.

Another problem common to tables is rust and pitting. Rust can cause pitting, as can someone using the table as a workbench and beating it with a hammer. Rust can easily be removed with steel wool, but pitting will require sanding or the use of a stone on your table.

Run-out and End Play

"Run-out" describes the condition of a shaft or spindle when it doesn't spin true. It is caused when the shaft is bent or not seated properly (as in a removeable shaper spindle), or when the bearings holding the shaft are misaligned. The amount of run-out is measured with a dial indicator.

On low-speed shafts, run-out may not be a problem; those that are bent can often be tapped straight on a press at a machine shop. High-speed shafts, on the other hand, may need to be re-machined. Major run-out (over a few thousandths) can be a major problem and dangerous on a machine like a shaper, molder, drill press, or tenoner. Mis-alignment of bearings can cause problems on machines like boring machines and table saws.

"End play" is caused by worn bearings or bearings that are loose in their housings. This is also checked with a dial indicator by putting it up to the end of a shaft and trying to pull the shaft back and forth. Let me make it clear that there is always a small amount of end play and run-out in any machine; there is also a small amount of flex in any shaft, but significant amounts will need to be tended to. Most bearings can be easily and inexpensively replaced, but not always. Some drill press bearings cannot be found today, and high-speed bearings (like shaper bearings) can easily cost $150 apiece. Babbitt bearings were generally used on machines prior to 1920-30; they are not easy to replace. They must be poured with molten babbitt material; this takes an expert, or at least a great deal of practice. While babbitt bearings can be superior—especially on machines like lathes and table saws—they require diligent lubrication, and babbitt, being soft, scores and degrades easily if the bearing becomes contaminated. End play in babbitt bearings is reduced by removing shims from under the bearing cap, but once the babbitt gets too thin, the shaft rubs on the casting and is ruined. Also, if the bearings get too hot, either from over-tightening the cap or from lack of lubrication, the babbitt will melt and run-out. Therefore, when buying a babbitt-bearing machine, it is critical to evaluate the condition and remaining life of the bearings.

To summarize, examine the machine thoroughly with good light. Turn all the cranks, spin all the shafts, check the bearings, check the motor phase requirements. Run the machine, if possible. Feel the table for vibration, listen for funny sounds, check for abuse and cracks in the casting. Again, don't let your enthusiasm cloud your judgment. A "free" machine can end up costing you a lot of time and money. If it is a great machine, it may be worth it. Otherwise, just say *no*.

MOVING HEAVY MACHINERY

I think at this time it might be worth saying a little about moving machinery. A machine that seems like the Rock of Gibralter on the shop floor can fall over surprisingly easily when you take the first turn in a truck. When a heavy piece of machinery falls over, something usually breaks or bends. The best thing to do is to disassemble the machine as much as possible before you attempt to move it. It's a good idea to remove tables from bases, outriggers, motors, and the like. Removing a motor will entail disconnecting wiring. Draw a little diagram so that later everything gets put back where it belongs. Tagging the ends can be a help as well. Always remove any delicate parts such as knobs, fences, guards, tool rests, etc. Always, for safety's sake, remove all cutters, blades, or anything else sharp. Always use gloves and watch your hands and feet. It is really easy to get into trouble with a heavy piece of machinery. Moving any machine is not worth severe injury. If it's too big to handle, get help. Dollies, hand trucks, peevee bars, pipes, and the like, can all be extremely helpful. A come-along or power winch can also be handy in moving machinery up a ramp. Rent a truck with a lift gate if you can; just be sure it's rated for the weight of your machine. When all else fails, auto movers and riggers can safely move your machine, although expect to pay a few hundred dollars unless you have friends in the business. Remember, many people have been injured when moving a machine that got out of control. Take the time to do it safely.

DISASSEMBLY AND ASSESSMENT

Once your machine is back at the shop, the first step is to disassemble it and fully assess its condition. This is when you begin to find out how good a deal you really made. It is very important when you disassemble machinery to make careful and accurate diagrams of how different sections go back together. Polaroid camera shots are helpful. It may seem very clear and obvious at the time, but over the course of a few days, you would be amazed at how confusing it all can get.

Take everything apart that is questionable, or that needs painting or cleaning, but remember, if it ain't broke, don't fix it! If you're compulsive, like me, you'll probably take everything apart anyway, but systems that are obviously fully operational don't need to be disassembled. I always take motors apart, though, because over the years oil and sawdust cake up on the inside and should be cleaned out.

As you take assemblies apart and make your diagrams, group the parts in different boxes. Small parts should go into cans or cups and be labeled. You should also start a list of parts that need to be repaired or replaced. Remember to write down the sequence in which things come apart. A lot of time is wasted in assembly when you put things together in the wrong sequence, only to realize later that it all has to come apart again so that a certain part can be fitted in.

Keep your eyes open for modifications or faulty assembly. Just because it was put together a certain way when you got it, doesn't mean that it's right. Someone who didn't have a clue may have worked on your machine before you. Use your head; if it doesn't work right, try to figure out what someone may have done wrong. Pay special attention to shafts, gears, bearings, and bushings. If a bearing is hard to turn, turns roughly, or has a lot

of play, replace it. Bushings with a lot of play should also be replaced. Examine gears for chipped and missing teeth. Check shafts that fit into bushings for excessive wear. Check for broken-off or stripped-out bolts. Drain the oil from gearboxes and check for metal shavings in the residue. Check the condition of V belts and replace where necessary. If there is more than one belt driving, be sure to order the belts in matched sets to minimize vibration. Examine the machine for signs of a catastrophic event that may have occured: a bent shaft, a chunk out of the table, burnt paint, or the like.

And, finally, be sensitive when taking things apart; you don't want to break anything. If bolts are frozen, soak them in a rust solvent, use a rubber mallet or wooden block to tap things apart, support parts so they don't fall when loosened — and don't force anything. If it's not coming apart, chances are you are not taking it apart correctly. Machines are built to come apart in a certain sequence. If you don't know the sequence, don't create problems by forcing it. Get some help. It would be impossible in one short chapter to describe all of the ways machinery comes apart, but here are a few tips that may prove helpful. Many parts are held together with set screws or allen screws. These will require an allen wrench to loosen. Pulleys often have more than one set screw recessed into the grooves of the pulley. In time, these can fill with gunk and become difficult to spot. So inspect the piece carefully. Set screws often tighten into a hole or dimple machined into a shaft, so be careful when you re-assemble to make sure it seats back into its recess.

Often, gears and other parts are held in place with tapered or split pins. These are sometimes ground flush to the gear body and can be hard to see. A split pin is hollow with a cut down one side and should tap out easily from either side, with the correct diameter straight punch. Tapered pins, as the name implies, are a larger diameter on one side than the other and can only come out from one side. Trying to get them out the other way will only tighten them. Therefore, inspect both sides to determine which is the smaller end and use your punch from that side only.

Most bearings are held in place with some sort of retainer, either a bolted-on cap, a threaded nut or ring, or a snap ring. Often, it is a combination of these. They must, of course, be removed before the shaft and bearing can come out. Bearings are press-fit onto the shaft and they also should be a snug fit into their housings. The shaft will have to be tapped out with a mallet or pressed out in a press, if it is really tight. Then the bearings will have to be removed from the shaft with a bearing puller. These tools can be rented if you don't already have them, or your local machine or automotive shop can do the job for you.

Some parts are held in place on tapered shafts, e.g., the wheels on my Oliver bandsaw. This can result in an incredibly tight fit and require a large puller for removal. Be aware when using presses and pullers that the accumulated mechanical force can result in something exploding or letting go. So always use extreme caution and full face protection. Be aware, also, that many parts are kept from binding to adjacent parts through the use of shims and spacers, so always include these in your diagram. Gears, pulleys, and the like, are kept from spinning on their shafts by the use of keys, either rectangular or half-round, that fit into keyways milled into the mating surfaces. These must be free of burrs and seated properly for reassembly. When removing threaded nuts and rings, always check the direction of the threads before disassembling. Sometimes, because of rotational force, these are threaded left hand, so that they tend to tighten rather than loosen during use. A good example is the nut that holds the sawblade tight on a table saw or radial arm saw. If you try to loosen these counter-clockwise, you will only end up tightening them. Check the end of the threaded shaft and see which way the threads are headed, if this is a question. Also, watch for spring-loaded subassemblies. If you are not careful, they will "fire" parts across the room.

Mating metal surfaces that are intended to hold fluids, such as gear boxes that contain a reservoir of gear oil, generally have gaskets between them to prevent oil from leaking. This gasket will probably disintegrate when you take the section apart. If this happens, you can buy gasket material at an automotive or industrial supply house, and cut a new one out with an x-acto knife. Alternatively, you can try a liquid gasket material product available at the same places. Remember, don't get frustrated; if it went together, it will come apart. Take your time to figure it out. Just blindly pounding on it with a big hammer will only create more problems.

REPAIRS/PARTS

Now that you have disassembled and assessed your machine, you should have a pretty good idea of what is missing and broken. It is to be hoped that you have been making a list and separating out pieces that need to be addressed.

Unless you are an expert welder, any cracked or broken pieces need to be taken to a competent welding or machine shop. Be sure that they understand how the part fits into the general picture: what is critical to the machine's operation and what is just structural or cosmetic. Any parts that need to be re-machined will also require a trip to the machine shop. Again, the more the machinist understands the tolerances of what he's machining, the better job he can do.

Bearings that need to be replaced should be taken to a bearing supplier. Generally, the bearing number is etched into the side of the bearing. If not, the supplier will need to know the thickness, interior diameter (ID) and exterior diameter (OD). Bearings come in different classes, so never replace a precision high speed bearing with a low speed bearing, or you will be rebuilding your machine sooner than you think. Many older bearings were open (meaning you can see the balls) and were lubricated externally through the use of grease fittings and oil cups or ports. You may want to keep these, or you may decide to replace them with the more modern sealed or "lubricated for life" bearings. Many low speed open bearings and bushings just need to be cleaned in solvent, blown out, and re-lubricated. The same applies to roller bearings, such as the bearings on bed and drive rollers on planers. Babbitt bearings, as mentioned earlier, should be re-poured by professionals if necessary.

Nuts and bolts can often be a problem. If a bolt is broken off, it will have to be drilled and removed with a tool called an extractor or drilled out completely. Taps should be run down into tight or rusty threaded bolt holes. Buggered threads on larger bolts can be corrected with a tapered needle file or thread restorer tool. Smaller bolts can have a die run down them.

If the manufacturer is still in business, missing parts can be ordered directly from them. Otherwise, industrial supply houses, or mail order suppliers like McMaster-Karr or Grangers, may have the replacement parts you need. Certainly almost any nut, bolt, gear, grease or oil fitting, sight glass, crank, handwheel, knob, pulley, or electrical part is available from these catalogs. Flat belts can be custom laced at many industrial supply houses, and almost any motor can be repaired or re-wired at your local motor repair shop. Almost any custom cutter can be fabricated for a price, and planer and jointer knives are readily available. Custom cutterheads can also be made or modified. Threaded boring bits and hollow chisel mortising sets are also easily available. Charles Schmidt in New Jersey is an excellent source for knives, blades, cutters, and cutterheads. If all else fails, a used machinery distributor, such as Carpenter's Machinery in York, Pennsylvania, or Rudolph Bass in Jersey City, may have the part you are looking for.

CLEANING AND DETAILING

Though many people don't seem to care what a machine looks like, to me it's important. I always am inspired to do better work when the machine is clean. The best time to clean, paint, and detail your machine is now, when it is disassembled. (If it is fairly clean to start with, you can skip the next step.)

On many old machines, the paint is deteriorating. To repaint, you will have to remove any loose paint and rust. There are many methods to accomplish this. If you are a purist and want to get down to bare metal, you can have the castings sand blasted. I generally use a tool called a scaler. This works off compressed air, which causes approximately a dozen steel pins to move in and out continually at high speed, quickly cleaning off any loose paint or rust. You can also use scrapers, hand-held wire brushes, or wire brushes that you can chuck into an electric drill. On really quality machines, uneven areas on the castings were filled and molded with body filler. It is not necessary to remove this unless it is loose.

After all loose paint and rust has been removed, it's time to put on the rubber gloves and wash the castings down with a solvent such as paint thinner, or a cleaning product like "pre-kleeno." I usually use a bristle brush and lots of paper towels until all greasy residue is removed. Then you must use masking tape and paper to cover all areas that do not get paint. These include the table surfaces, mating areas, areas machined for shafts, bearings, mounting blocks, trunions, and the like. If you are down to bare metal, you must start with a bare metal primer. I use a good quality paint from a spray can. Spray the primer on lightly. It is better to apply several coats than to have your paint run.

After the primer dries, you can pick a color and start to paint. This is the fun part. Suddenly, what was old and decrepit-looking, begins to look clean and new. If you're a purist, you may want to have a paint shop mix the original color for you. If you do, you will need to use a spray gun and compressor to paint your piece. Allow parts to dry completely before turning them over to paint the other side. Also be sure to wear a chemical respirator and to provide adequate ventilation. The fumes are quite noxious and also quite flammable. Paint fumes building up in a confined area are an explosion waiting to happen.

Never paint over decals, brass name plates, or brass height, depth, speed indicators. Instead clean them carefully, polish the brass with fine steel wool, and then mask them before painting.

After you've finished painting, remove the mask and spray the parts with clear lacquer. If there are wooden parts, clean them with solvent and medium steel wool, and then oil, varnish, or wax them, depending on your preference. When the painting is done, remove the tape and clean up any overspray with steel wool or a razor blade. To complete the job, I like to highlight any lettering in the casting (such as the manufacturer's name and location) by hand with black paint and a small detail paint brush.

RE-ASSEMBLY

Now is the time to slow down and try to get it right the first time. If you feel you are in a little over your head, try to get your hands on a machinery manual. If the manufacturer is still in business, it may sell or give you the schematics for the machine. If you know someone who has the same, or a similar, machine, check it out. Otherwise, refer carefully to your disassembly notes, and try to think through the proper sequence.

Press your bearings carefully onto the shaft, applying an even, steady pressure so as not to cock the bearing on the shaft or in its housing. Always press the bearing on its inner or outer race and not

on the area in between. If it just won't go, use dry ice to "shrink" the shaft, warm the bearing to expand it, and then try again. Always be sensitive to torque and pressure. Cast iron is very brittle and cracks easily. Learn the difference between snug, tight, and broken off. Keep your eyes open. It's that last quarter turn that get's you in trouble every time. Keep a fine file or diamond file handy and make sure there are no burrs on shafts, keyways, keys, etc. Lubricate everything with grease as you assemble it. Don't force anything. If it's not going back together, there is a reason. Is the set screw backed out enough; is there a little mushroomed metal on the shaft? Is everything seated properly; is a part turned around the wrong way? Does the shaft turn smoothly on its new bearings? Is the set screw seated securely in its dimple? Take your time, don't overcommit, take one step at a time, and think ahead. If it's not working, put it aside until tomorrow, or get some help. There is no magic in machinery; no evil spirits. That's part of the beauty of machinery. It is purely mechanical cause and effect. It it's a good machine, there is an answer to your problem.

Once your machine is basically together, it is going to require fine tuning and adjustment. Most machines with moving tables have adjustable gibs. These are metal plates that adjust for the wear that, over the years, accumulates as these parts move against each other. The adjustment is done with a row of set screws held in position with lock nuts. To adjust, loosen the lock nuts, bring up the set screws, then back them off until the table moves easily without play. Then, without allowing the set screws to move, tighten the lock nuts. This may take some trial and error.

On machines with V belts and pulleys, it is necessary to align the pulleys carefully with a straight edge, and then tension the V belt so that there is about ¾" deflection. With flat belts , it's necessary to align the drums so that the belt tracks true. Babbitt bearings must be adjusted with shims so that the shaft turns freely without play. It is also important that the oil channels cut into the babbitt are clean so the oil can circulate through the entire bearing. Stops and limits must be adjusted so that tilting assemblies start at 90° and stop at 45°. Cam locking systems, such as tail stocks and tool posts on lathes must be adjusted so they achieve maximum locking power. Tables need to be adjusted so that they are on the same plane, parallel or perpendicular to the cutterhead. Fences and guards need to be adjusted to ensure accuracy and safety. Make sure your wiring is safe and secure. If this is a question, consult an electrician.

Never turn a machine on until you've spun everything by hand, gone to all the limits without the cutter contacting anything, and lubricated everything that needs lubricating. Then, stand back and give it a try. If all has been done right, it should purr like a kitten; if not, shut it off immediately. If it is making a horrible loud noise, chances are that something that's spinning is contacting something that's not, possibly the casting, guard, or cover. Maybe something wasn't tightened down well and is now spinning on its shaft. If there is excessive vibration, check to make sure the pulleys are aligned. Is the machine seated securely on the floor? Is the cutterhead out of balance, or, in the case of the bandsaw, are the wheels balanced? Is a bearing loose in its housing or shaft? If your machine gets too hot to touch, it's generally a bearing problem. Does the bearing spin freely; is it getting lubrication? If your machine won't start, it's probably electrical. Is there power to the machine; is the switch or magnetic starter operating; is the motor wired correctly? With machine restoration, especially when there is no manual available, you don't always get it right the first time, but if your stick with it and get help when necessary, you will figure it out.

MAINTENANCE

Once you get your machine running properly, it is important not to forget periodic maintenance.

How much you will need to maintain your machine depends on how it was constructed and how much use it gets.

Lubrication is the prime consideration. Sealed bearings will not require lubrication, but open bearings and bushings, babbitt bearings, and gear boxes will. On machines with grease fittings, it will be necessary to use the appropriate grease and a grease gun. Oil cups will need an occasional squirt of 10w - 40 motor oil, as will bushings. Babbitt bearings need to be oiled frequently during use and often have adjustable drip oilers for this purpose. Gear boxes need to be kept filled to the correct level with clean gear oil, and high speed bearings need a thin high speed oil. Often there is a sight glass to allow you to monitor the oil level in these machines. All metal-to-metal moving parts should be greased with lithium grease or a dry spray such as silicon. Tables and fences should be kept waxed. Switches and magnetic starters should be opened occasionally and the sawdust blown out. Power cords should be checked for insulation damage, and belts for cracking and fraying. Check the guards to make sure they are doing what they need to do. Lastly, listen to your machines. Once you get used to the way they sound, small changes can easily be distinguished and can be early warning signals for trouble.

INDIVIDUAL MACHINES

Since most of this chapter is filled, out of necessity, with rather general information, I thought it might be useful to include a short segment on issues specific to individual types of woodworking machinery. For simplicity's sake, I have arranged the machines in four categories: machines that cut, shape, sand, and bore wood. (Of course, many of these machines function in more than one category, and there are many more specialized machines that I have omitted entirely.)

MACHINES THAT CUT WOOD

Tablesaws

The tablesaw is arguably the heart of the woodworking shop. It is necessary, for accurate work, that the blade be made square to the table top and parallel to the slots milled in the table to accommodate the slides. It is also important that the fence be straight and square and can be made parallel to the blade. The blade should tilt with minimum effort to 45°. On some saws this is accomplished by tilting the *table*, which is not as desireable. The blade should elevate easily from below the table surface to full height. Direct drive tablesaws are generally quieter and more powerful, but they do not allow the blade to be elevated as high as on belt- or chain-driven machines. Some saws have sliding or rolling tables to aid in cutting large panels and long boards.

It is important that the washers that clamp the blade are flat and that they sit square on the shaft, otherwise the blade will oscillate. This should be checked with a dial indicator, but on the shaft, not on the blade, as the blade is often tensioned so that it only spins true at speed. The accessories to the saw are the fence, mitre slides (usually two of these on better saws), saw insert, blade nut and wrenches, blade guard, splitter, and blades.

Radial Arm Saws

Radial arm saws are fairly complicated machines because of the many pivots and adjustments necessary to achieve accurately their full range of motion. The motor and blade assembly should roll smoothly down the arm and there should be a means to eliminate play in this travel. The bearings that the motor yoke rides on may be difficult to find. The entire arm should elevate and pivot, and the motor should swivel and pivot in its yoke. All pivot points should be adjustable for wear and all should have positive stops. It is also important that the table can be aligned parallel to the full forward and back, left to right travel of the blade. Accessories are blade guard and blades.

Jig Saws

Jig saws are relatively simple machines. The greater the throat opening (distance between blade and casting), the more versatile it is. Older style jig saws relied on a mechanical movement that pulled a blade straight down against a spring, with the spring pulling the blade back up on the upstroke. It is my opinion that modern parallel arm jig saws, based upon the really early wooden models, are superior, but the old style worked well. Generally the lower bushing that supports the shaft with the bottom blade clamp wears out first, so check for play there. There should also be an adjustable support foot that holds the work down against the table. The table should tilt, and there is usually a tube and bellows assembly whose function is to blow dust away from the saw cut.

Thickness Planers

Thickness planers are fairly complex machines. It is critical that the tables are flat and can be adjusted parallel to the cutterhead. The cutterhead must be balanced. The feed rollers usually are driven by a gear box and should be adjusted parallel to the table and at the right height to feed the work through, before and after the cut. These should be variable speed and spring-loaded with adjustable tension. The pressure bar is at the heart of the planer, tucked just behind the cutterhead. It must be straight and adjustable for a smooth cut. The bed rollers should be adjustable in height and parallel to the table. There is also a chipbreaker on many machines. The table should raise and lower smoothly through its whole travel. This all may seem rather complicated—a lot of parts, bearings, and adjustments—but it's mostly a question of understanding the concept.

Joiners

Joiners are simple machines, but they must be set up accurately for good results. The most critical factor is the alignment of the infeed and outfeed tables with each other and with the cutter-head. Each table must be in the same plane front and back and side to side, even though they are at different heights.

The cutterhead must be balanced. Usually both tables raise and lower on ways with adjustable gibs. Sometimes just the infeed table moves, and the outfeed is fixed, making it necessary to set the knives to the height of the rear table. Often both tables also pull straight out away from the cutterhead to facilitate changing knives or to give the operator access to the dust collection chute, should it become clogged.

The ways for table height adjustment are either cast into the machine or are four blocks, one on each corner of the table, that are bolted on. If the tables are flat and are supported in each corner with a bolt on ways, they can always be shimmed into alignment with each other and the cutterhead. If the ways are cast into the base and have warped, the tables can't be aligned, and you will never get a true surface. The fence should be relatively straight and square to the table. It should also tilt to 45°. There should be a good guard on both sides of the fence that covers the cutter with the fence in any position. Avoid square cutterheads if you plan to use the machine; they are known to pull hands into the cutters. A knife grinding attachment for either a joiner or planer is a definite plus.

Band Saws

Band saws can be very trying machines because of the adjustments necessary to get the upper and lower wheels into exact alignment with one another. On some saws there is no adjustment, so you're stuck with what you get. If the arm on the casting warps, you will never get the blade to track correctly. The wheels are generally covered with rubber tires that are cemented on. In time, the rubber gets brittle and cracks. These tires are available for most saws, but it takes some experience to glue them on and get them crowned correctly. There are places, however, that will do

this for you. The blades are tensioned by a spring and tracked with a knob that tilts the top wheel. The blade runs through guide blocks which wear out fairly quickly, and is supported from behind with bearings or another hardened block. The upper guides are supported by an arm that moves up and down parallel to the blade to accommodate various thicknesses of stock.

The table should be relatively flat and should tilt easily to 45°. It is important that both wheels be balanced, have adequate guards, and that all open blade areas be guarded as well. Many large bandsaws are equipped with a brake. Accessories might include a mitre slide and a fence.

MACHINES THAT SHAPE WOOD

Lathes

Lathes are very simple machines. If the bed is straight and sound, and if the headstock center lines up with the tailstock center, it will probably work. Quick release toolposts and tailstocks are a plus. The quill in the tailstock should crank in and out smoothly and lock securely. The headstock spindle should be concentric and threaded to accept a faceplate or chuck. It should also be threaded on the outboard end to accommodate a faceplate for outboard turning. Lathes generally have variable speeds, and it is a benefit if you can adjust the speed without turning the machine off to change belts.

Lathe bearings take a lot of load from a lot of different directions, so they are prone to wearing out. Pattern lathes have a slide rest, similar to those found on machine lathes, on which cutters can be mounted for mechanical turning. Often you also offset the tailstock so that tapers can be machined as well. Accessories to the lathe include additional toolposts, tool rests, centers, faceplates, chucks, and turning tools.

Tenoners

Industrial tenoners perform a series of operations simultaneously, and for this reason can be fairly complicated to restore. Usually they have two opposing tenoning cutterheads, one or both of them being adjustable. The cutterhead generally house skewed rabbeting knives and serrated scoring blades. Usually there are coping cutterheads that adjust in relation to the tenoning heads. Often there is a sawblade arbor assembly that serves to cut the tenon to length. The work itself is clamped in position onto a rolling table. On older machines all these different assemblies are driven by flat belts that also have their own shafts and bearing assemblies. On newer machines there can be individual motors for each of these shafts. This all adds up to a lot of shafts, bearings, and adjustments. These machines, however, can be extremely quick and efficient when set up properly.

Shapers

Shapers are quite simple machines—basically just oversized inverted routers. Because of their high operating speeds, it is imperative that the spindle runs true, with minimal run-out. Some machines have one fixed spindle; others have interchangeable spindles of different diameters. A minimum diameter of 1 1/8" - 1 1/4" is needed to safely spin large or heavy cutters. The spindle should be carefully checked near the top with a dial indicator. A run-out of over 3-4 thousandths can be a problem. The large bearings that support the spindle assembly are high speed precision bearings and can easily cost over $100 apiece.

The spindle should raise and lower easily with the use of a hand wheel. On some shapers, the spindle or table tilts to 45°. The table should be relatively flat and generally have removeable inserts that fit around the spindle opening to accommodate different size cutters. Some shapers have

two or three spindles. Many have variable speeds, usually achieved by means of a stepped pulley.

Direct drive shapers will need a transformer to bring them up to speed. Accessories include fence, table inserts, additional spindles, guards and hold-downs, tools to insert and remove the spindle, spacers, and shaper cutters and cutterheads.

Molders

Molders can be very complicated machines, and their restoration should probably be left to an expert unless you have a lot of experience. However, some molders are simpler (basically surfacers) and in this respect are similar to joiners and planers.

MACHINES THAT SAND WOOD

Stroke Sanders

Older stroke sanders generally consist of two cast iron pedestals, which support the drive and idler rollers, with a rolling table in between. Some stroke sanders have four rollers instead of two, one of which pivots and is counterweighted. This allows the belt to change length when sanding convex and concave shapes. The table should roll, and raise and lower, easily. There should also be an easy means to track the belt. It's all very simple, but it can take a while to set it all up properly. Sanding belts of any width, length, or grit can be custom-fabricated through an abrasive distributor.

Vertical Drum Sanders

Drum sanders are very simple and useful machines. Oscillating drum sanders have a mechanism, generally immersed in an oil bath, that raises and lowers the spindle as it revolves. This feature gives more life to the sanding sheaves. Better sanders have a variety of different diameter drums, whose tapered ends fit into a tapered recess in the spindle. The table should have different inserts, like the shaper table. It generally tilts to 45°.

Disc Sanders

Disc sanders are also very simple machines. It is important for accurate work that the disc is very flat. This needs to be checked with an accurate straight edge. If it is not flat, and it is thick enough, it can be machined flat on a machine lathe. The table should be well supported and square to the disc. It should also tilt to 45°. On some machines, the table also cranks downward to facilitate changing the disc. Try peel and stick discs; they are worth the extra cost.

Horizontal Belt Sanders

These sanders rely on a flat, straight platen for accurate work; this should be carefully checked with a straightedge. The belt should track easily and stay put. The table should be flat, and square to the platen, and should tilt to 45°. Some sanders prolong wear life by oscillating the belt. Other models tilt the table along the length of the belt to increase the wear area. Most edge sanders have a table by the idler drum to utilize its curved shape, for sanding concave surfaces. A useful accessory is a mitre stop that pivots on the table.

MACHINES THAT BORE WOOD

Drill Press

This machine is essential to any wood or metal shop. Most are belt-driven and very simple; gear-driven models, while more industrial, are also more complicated. The bearings that allow the spindle to revolve in the quill, and the bushings that support the vertical movement of the quill, are always suspect. These parts may prove very difficult to find for older machines.

Radial drill presses are subject to most of the considerations associated with radial arm saws. On some drill presses, the *table* moves up and down; on some the *head;* on some, both. On the latter machines, the head is usually keyed, so it can be moved up and down without changing its alignment to the work. Often the table tilts 45° either way to allow for drilling angled holes without jigs. There should be a stop system to control drilling depth, and a way to lock the quill should the need arise. The capacity of the chuck should be a consideration, but the chuck should be easy to replace, if necessary. Often there are slots milled in the table to accommodate clamp and vise mounting.

Horizontal Boring Machines

Working on horizontal boring machines with more than one spindle can be quite frustrating if things aren't going just right. There are two ways these machines work; either the spindles are fixed and the table moves in and out, or the table is fixed and the spindles move. Either way, the spindles move closer or further away from each other to allow different hole spacing. The table also moves up and down to accommodate different stock thicknesses. Keeping all these different movements in correct relation to each other, to the degree of accuracy necessary for precision work, can take some doing. If it's not a good machine, you may never get it right. If it *is* a good machine, it can really work wonderfully. Good machines come with an easily adjustable way to clamp the work to the table, and a series of stops for repetitive set-ups. Most machines use brad-tipped drills with threaded ends, while others have universal chucks. Most of this tooling is still readily available.

Mortising Machines

Mortising machines come in many different styles. Early machines were foot-powered; some had wooden springs and a static cutter that was designed to square up a pre-drilled mortise.

Later machines had active cutters, either oscillating, chain saw type, or, most commonly, hollow chisels with drill bits revolving within. These are driven into the work, either by foot power or a mechanical drive assembly. The table needs to be heavy to resist the pressure of the chisel and should slide easily side to side with a handcrank. There need to be stops and hold-downs as well. Power hollow chisel mortisers usually have an adjustable length of stroke, and the drill speed is also adjustable. It is important that the chisels be sharp and the drill be securely chucked. If the drill stops turning and the chisel continues to be forced into the work, both the chisel and the work will be ruined.

CONCLUSION

Since the day when I (not without some small amount of trepidation) took apart my first ma-

chine, I have restored many, many machines. Some I have kept, some I have sold, but with each one my experience and confidence grew. Once you understand the basic concepts, woodworking machinery is surprisingly simple. This is not to say I don't get thrown some curves occasionally, but such is life. Now I am considered (deservedly or not) something of a local expert on machine restoration and adjustment. I have learned a lot, with a lot more left to learn. What surprises me, though, is how many of my fellow shop owners are afraid even to take a router apart to change the bearings. Therefore, I offer this chapter in the hope that it will instill in its readers enough cautious optimism to attempt a simple restoration (and then possibly a more complicated one), and thereby save from the scrap heap a beautiful and functional relic of America's industrial heyday.

David Pollak
Creative Woodcraft
Dover, New Jersey

A Note to the Reader

Though there have been some 240 American manufacturers of woodworking machinery since the late 1830's, I'm afraid half of them will remain mysterious names cast into a machine's iron frame. No one will ever know anything of their founders or the company's history.

My goal is to gather, save, and preserve as much historical material as possible before it's too late. When I learn of a company's deliberate destruction of its machinery blueprints, catalogs, manuals, press books, etc., it breaks my heart. And it happens all too often.

The appearance and publication date of future volumes depends largely on how much and how soon the author can obtain research data. Therefore I am interested in acquiring by loan, gift, or photocopy any and all documents, catalogs, manuals, photos, personal reminiscences, trade journals, etc., pertaining to woodworking machinery and/or its manufacturers.

Write to the author at 402 East Bucyrus Street, Crestline, Ohio 44827. No phone calls please. All useful help and information will be acknowledged.

Dana Batory

BIBLIOGRAPHY

Bale, M. Povis. *Woodworking Machinery.* London: Crosby Lockwood & Co., 1880.

Brown, Nelson Courtlandt. *Lumber Manufacture, Conditioning, Grading, Distribution, and Use.* New York: John Wiley & Sons, Inc., 1947.

Byrn, Edward W. *The Progress of Invention in the Nineteenth Century.* New York: Munn & Co., 1900.

Collins, A. Frederick. *A Bird's Eye View of Invention.* New York, Thomas Y. Crowell Company, 1926.

Hjorth, Herman. *Machine Woodworking.* Milwaukee: The Bruce Publishing Co., 1937.

Mansfield, Judson H. "Woodworking Machinery, History of Development, 1852-1952." *Journal of American Society of Mechanical Engineers,* vol. 74, December 1952, pp.983-995.

Roe, Joseph Witham. *English and American Tool Builders.* New York: McGraw-Hill Book Co., 1916.

Sims, William L. *Two Hundred Years of History and Evolution of Woodworking Machinery.* Burton Lazars: Walders Press, 1985.

Wallace, J.D. and Wallace, Margaret S. "From the Master Cabinetmakers to Woodworking Machinery." *Transactions, The American Society of Mechanical Engineers,* January-April 1930, pp. 13-21.

Back issues of the following:
The Home Craftsman
The Hub
The Industrial-Arts Magazine
Industrial Arts and Vocational Education
Popular Homecraft
The Woodworker